VIV

£1.60

VIVIANS

*

M. V. Hughes

Oxford   New York

OXFORD UNIVERSITY PRESS

Oxford University Press, Walton Street, Oxford OX2 6DP

Oxford New York Toronto
Delhi Bombay Calcutta Madras Karachi
Petaling Jaya Singapore Hong Kong Tokyo
Nairobi Dar es Salaam Cape Town
Melbourne Auckland

and associated companies in
Beirut Berlin Ibadan Nicosia

Oxford is a trade mark of Oxford University Press

First published by Oxford University Press 1935
First issued as an Oxford University Press paperback 1980
Reprinted 1984, 1987

British Library Cataloguing in Publication Data

Hughes, Mary Vivian
Vivians.
1. Vivian family
I. Title
929'.2'0942 CS439.V6 80–40522
ISBN 0–19–281303–X

Reproduced, printed and bound in Great Britain by
J. W. Arrowsmith Ltd, Bristol

CONTENTS

ONE

TWO SISTERS

§ 1

THIS is the story of a woman who lived from the reign of George IV into the reign of George V. She did no single astounding thing, and yet her life as a whole was an extraordinary achievement. Everything that happened to her family and friends happened to her. Without the impetus of religious fervour, without any display of unselfishness, she wove into her own interests all the excitements, tragedies, joys, and petty worries of those whom she loved, and, most intensely of all, she lived through everything that affected her sister Mary.

Outside the family there were five men who entered fatefully into the lives of these two sisters, and their names have been taken as distinguishing marks for the various episodes of the story. The men themselves are depicted solely as they appeared in the eyes of the women. A knowledge of the facts throughout has been almost entirely due to a long and close intimacy with the women. They were the more reliable in that they had no desire to let any one know their story, or to talk about their affairs. Mary, the elder sister, had a genius for keeping things to herself, while Tony had all the will but not the same power. Tony therefore was the fount of most of the information. But there was a value even in Mary's reticence, for it is the ultra-reserved people who are apt to give themselves away by a chance word, a smothered

smile, a sigh, a favourite quotation (seeming to them imper-
sonal), a flash of temper, or even a faint hesitation about
answering some idle question. Like stage directions these
hints, though few, are all the more significant. By such give-
aways therefore Mary contributed almost as much as Tony,
but rather atmosphere and feeling than actual events.

Victorian chronologically through most of their lives,
these two sisters were pre-Victorian in spirit, with a general
outlook more closely resembling our own than that of the
intervening period. The proprieties, restrictions, and narrow
conventions of town life did not cast their dull pall over
robust country life. At any rate, in such a remote corner as
Cornwall these artificial manners and clogs on freedom never
at any time succeeded in taking hold, because reality above
all things was required in a region swilled by the wild and
wasteful ocean.

The emancipation of women had not occurred and a
Cornish girl would have wondered what it meant, for her
life was almost as free as that of a girl to-day. If she could
not go to her garage, start her own car and dash about
England, she could go to the stable, saddle her horse herself,
and go wherever fancy suggested. And as in the present
day, and not in the days of propriety, she could go entirely
unescorted. If the excitement of aviation and wireless and
electricity was lacking, the first locomotives, steamboats, and
gas-lighting were quite as miraculous and as hazardous.

§ 2

The early surroundings of Mary and Tony were wealthy
in the best sense of the word. Their father, Joseph Vivian,

2

was highly esteemed in the country round, and always known as 'Cap'n Vivian'. Captain indeed he was of all his numerous belongings, for he took a personal interest in every one who served him, and used his wealth lavishly not only for the benefit of his own family but also for the well-being of his dependants. An enjoyable life and the goodwill of his neighbours were far more to him than any kind of self-aggrandizement.

A Man of Tin, he owned or managed or had shares in nearly all the mines of the district surrounding Carn Brea, a hill near Camborne with an ancient monument on it that could be seen for miles around. Grouped about the foot of this romantic hill, the mines reared their smoking chimneys like a comely forest. They were eloquent to Cap'n Vivian of brisk trade and prosperous new ventures, of the many miners going cheerfully to work, and of the countless other men to be found in all parts of the world, who had emigrated from Cornwall and were showing foreigners how to set about the job.

There was another side to this picture. The chimneys spoke to him too of the dangers always awaiting these men who worked continually underground, the risks they ran, as much from their own carelessness as from faulty machinery. When a young mining-engineer, full of enthusiasm for his work, he himself had suffered a serious accident. A steel drill fell down a shaft and struck him on the shoulder, obliging him to lie on his back for many a weary week. He had to undergo an operation in the days before the general use of anaesthetics, and he used to say that he bore the agony of the surgeon's knife only by picturing to himself the horrible alternative—not death, but disablement. It became one of his chief ambitions to have a son who would become a clever surgeon and be able to find means for alleviating such torture of body and mind.

Shortly after the end of the war with Napoleon, within a mile or so of these mines, in a sheltered, well-wooded valley, Cap'n Vivian created a home for his young wife, Nancy. Creation is not too grand a word for the way in which he adapted an ancient farm-house, added to it a new Georgian house, and bit by bit laid out a long drive bordered by different kinds of trees, as well as lawns, orchards, flower-gardens and kitchen-gardens, including a running brook and several ponds. The large farm, too, he maintained so as to get the utmost yield from its many acres of corn and pasture land, and its innumerable sheep, cattle, pigs, and poultry. Horses for all purposes stocked his stables. A forge and a water-mill completed his sense of independence.

This independence of the outside world became his favourite boast. But not even the ample and varied life arising from his mining and farming was enough to satisfy his craving for adventure, and he seized every opportunity that mining afforded for foreign travel. When young he had volunteered to go abroad for mine-prospecting, when others were reluctant; and when he was his own master he could easily find a pretext for a tin or copper mission. He became quite a grand figure, ruling like some feudal lord or Old Testament patriarch over a small army of miners, clerks, farm-labourers, gardeners, grooms, domestic staff, and a family of ten children that arrived in due course.

One weak spot he had. No smallest fault could he ever

see in his eldest daughter. He allowed her to do whatever she liked. This would not have mattered so much had her mother not been almost as bad. She was born on Furry Day, that ancient festival of fertility that is still celebrated every May 8th in Helston. To the superstitious Cornish mind it was the happiest omen to arrive with the goddess Flora—an omen of lifelong gaiety of spirit. From her earliest years Mary was accustomed to being the top of the market. She had an absurd way of fascinating everybody. Before she could speak plainly she would toddle into the kitchen to cast her criticism on the cooking, into the garden to give orders for more pink flowers, or into the yard to be hoisted on to one of the horses for a ride. Sammy, the youngest groom, when reprimanded for this, would plead 'there was no denyin' of she'. And he also comforted Nancy with the assurance that a horse will do no harm to you if you aren't afraid. Always ready to see the bright side Nancy accepted this doctrine, and allowed the child to indulge in her fearless pastime.

A few more years turned her into a little sprite, with hazel eyes and hair almost black, with a ready come-back for any witty sally from her father, with ready pangs of sympathy for any creature in trouble, and a sudden captivating laugh. On the rare occasions when a scolding was positively necessary, after she had been leading a small brother into some dare-devilry, her father would have reaction of spirit and come up to her after the storm to slip a sovereign into her hand. Most reprehensible this, but the coin, beyond being pretty to look at, meant nothing to her. Up to her dying day she never took the faintest interest in money nor had any notion of managing it. Often enough, when some serious delinquency of Mary's came to light, it turned out that for some mysterious reason her eldest brother William was responsible for it, at least according to their father's opinion. William was consequently thrashed, in spite of Mary's protests. She would then throw her arms round him with tears, say it was all her fault, and thank him so prettily for taking her thrashing that he would say it didn't matter a bit.

Nancy failed to stop the spoiling, but kept hoping that another daughter would come to share it and set things right. But three more boys were born in succession, making the situation more pronounced. At last, to every one's delight, a second daughter arrived. Most of all to Mary's delight, for she was intoxicated at having a baby sister, and mothered her so tenderly that very soon little Annie was among her adorers and ready to join in all her escapades in lane and field and garden. Finding 'Annie' a poor name for carrying a distance, Mary lengthened it to 'Antonina', which was shortened to 'Tony' for household use.

It was as well that Tony was not with Mary on one of her garden investigations. Coming upon some laburnum pods Mary split them open and was pleased to see something 'as good as peas'. She ate freely. For two days she was violently ill, and on the third there seemed to her distracted parents no hope of her recovery from a state of utter exhaustion. Not very long before they had lost one of their sons from a sudden attack of fever, and they supposed that this must be something of the same kind, for Mary had not told about the laburnum pods—was indeed too ill. When Nancy had tried all her usual restoratives in vain, her son

Nicholas, a serious little boy of nine, ventured into the sick room.

'Mother,' said he, 'I think she must have been eating something. If I were you I wouldn't give her anything at all, but just keep her warm and quiet. Watch her, and she will come round all right, like that sick calf I cured the other day.'

Nancy was wise enough to follow her little boy's advice, even allowing him to take turns with her in watching by Mary's bed. He ordered a bottle of hot water to be put at her feet, removed the heavy clothing on her, opened the window, dismissed Nancy to take a rest, and took up his position by the bed, as solemn as any doctor. After an hour or so, when Nancy came softly back, he was able to report proudly that Mary had opened her eyes and smiled, and was now in an easy sleep.

This episode was not of a kind to check the spoiling. Cap'n Vivian and Nancy agreed that the only thing for Mary was a boarding school, where she would be obliged to give and take with other girls of her own age. So she was dispatched to a school at Falmouth—not too far away. Of her own age many of the girls certainly were, but not of her ability, and her school report at the end of the year was glowing. This, added to Mary's own amusing description of the style of work, made it evident that she knew more than her teachers. Cap'n Vivian burst out, 'I don't care what it costs, Nancy, she shall go to the best school in England.'

Bath in those days was the last word in fashion, for education as for everything else. The most highly recommended school to be found there was chosen for Mary.

The cost was certainly high, but the school was more worth the money than many an expensive modern one. The number of pupils was strictly limited to six, who led a natural and jolly life together. Teaching was carried out almost entirely by visiting masters, for women in those days were not sufficiently learned for the task. The girls were expected to speak no language but French through the working day when chatting together. This they did, mainly because they were not supervised in the matter, or punished if they didn't. In this way French was absorbed, but Latin was taught more seriously. In addition to the usual accomplishments of music and drawing, an astonishing amount of stiff reading was required, and the girls became acquainted with such authors as Gibbon, Hume, Locke, and Berkeley, and able to discuss them. Probably the object of this was to provide some sensible background for conversation, for it is doubtful whether any aim beyond enabling the girls to shine socially entered into the scheme of the headmistress. The Bible class that was conducted every Saturday evening was a part of general culture. Manners and deportment were always the main concern, and by visits to other houses in Bath the girls were taught not only how to entertain, but also how to be entertained. As preparation for foreign travel they were often required to converse as best they could with some French, Spanish, or Italian visitor, invited to the house for this purpose.

In every subject Mary was easily the best, often having to be instructed separately by one of the visiting professors. The others didn't mind being outshone, for her high spirits made her a general favourite. They gave her the nickname

8

of 'Eclipse', after the famous Derby winner, of whom it was said 'Eclipse first, the rest nowhere'. As a rule the girls addressed one another by their surnames, and one of them had the magnificent name of Claringbull. Mary, with her name Vivian, her dark complexion, and slightly aquiline nose, was frequently taken for an Italian.

Meanwhile Tony's education at home had been along quite different lines. She was gradually learning all the details of house-management, how to feed poultry, make butter, cure pork, and of course how to cook and sew. Since her birth the family had been increased by a boy and three more girls, so there was no lack of occupation. Although innocent of Latin and philosophy she had the run of her father's good library, and read extensively as her fancy led her.

When Mary returned from Bath, 'finished', she and Tony made ideal companions, for each had what the other had missed. Although Tony was impressed by the account of what Mary had been taught, Mary soon found that she was far behind Tony in some ways, not only in domestic lore but also in general literature. Mary soon picked up enough knowledge of cooking and poultry-managing to relieve Nancy and Tony of a good deal of their work, and this left time for the two girls to have long walks and rides together. Their childish delight in each other had now grown into a comradeship that was to be lifelong. Tony was a greedy recipient of everything Mary could pass on of what she had learned at school, but enjoyed most the little gossipy bits about Bath. She had been reading Miss Austen's Tales, and actually knew Milsom Street and several other places that Mary mentioned. She liked to hear of the 'elegant' life, how the young ladies were made to eat heartily before going to a party so that their appetites should be genteel, how they were instructed to leave something on their plates, however attractive the dish, how they had to practise making graceful curtseys, getting into a carriage with the right foot first, and details of table manners.

'It all sounds rather silly,' said Tony after Mary had given her an amusing description one day of how Claringbull had been quite unable to curtsey deep enough, for she was of a generous build. 'And were you taught to swoon?'

'No, thank goodness; we were definitely warned against such a thing. Perhaps Madame, as we called her, had been as much charmed with Anne Elliot as we are. Perhaps she had discovered for herself that men are not so fond of fainting women when it comes to the point. She was no fool, I tell you. She gave us some useful hints in manners that we might not have thought of for ourselves. For one thing we were told to avoid the objectionable habit of repeating a person's name continually in conversation.'

Tony laughed assent. 'One could almost classify people by that. Those who keep on "yes, Miss Vivian, no, Miss Vivian", and those who mercifully allow you to forget yourself.'

'Another hint on manners sounded silly to me till I thought it over: if a man's foot touches yours, your natural response is to draw your foot away; do not do so immediately.'

Tony couldn't see the point of this, and wanted to know if any explanations were vouchsafed.

'None at all. Bits of experience of life were thrown out to us, just as you throw meal to the chicken. The best way, I think; better for the chicken than having the food stuffed into the beak. And we should have got so tired of having things explained that we shouldn't have listened. As it is these odd sayings stick in my mind. For instance, here's a simple rule for making yourself agreeable: Never pass on the unpleasant; always pass on the pleasant. I've stuck to that and find it answers.'

'It sounds all right. But I've heard you snap out disagreeable remarks often enough.'

'Snapping out doesn't matter, life would be dull without a bit of snappiness. It's passing on that is so serious. A compliment at second-hand is enchanting, isn't it? And an ill-natured remark passed on leaves you defenceless—enraged in general, with no one to attack.'

'I suppose you girls discussed these things in private?'

'We did when there was anything uncertain. Some of the bits of worldly wisdom were quite obvious. Such as "Beware of people who are more pleasant in your house than in their own". We didn't discuss the fact, but we had some difficulty in finding the reason for it.'

'It's what father says—"inhospitable people are the very devil".'

'There was one rule thrown at us that gave us considerable bother: "treat an enemy like a friend, and a friend like an enemy". Fortunately Madame had added under her breath "because you never know". That gave me a clue.'

'What did you make of it then?'

'I took it as a hint to be reserved—always—not to be

too confidential with a friend, and not too unbridled with a foe, because you never know when the positions will be reversed.'

'I expect the others took your explanation. What sort of girls were they?'

'Very pleasant, all from families of good position. I made no special friends, but I liked them all, particularly one rather quiet girl, who said very little and seemed thoughtful. When we were all imagining one day the kind of life we should like to lead, what was my astonishment to hear this girl assert that she would like to be a woman of easy virtue!'

'Gracious! what did you say?'

'We were all rather taken aback, made no comment, and talked of something else. It was an eye-opener to me as to the curiosities of character one may come across in unexpected quarters.'

'And what sort of future did you fancy for yourself?'

'Oh, to travel—anywhere—across the sea—to find adventure somewhere.'

'That's not me,' said Tony. 'I would like to live all my life here, looking after everything.'

'But you would like to be married?'

'Oh yes, I suppose, some time or other, and have lots of children.'

'Sounds a bit tame. Me for a bit of life first.'

TWO

JOHN

§ 1

Not two years had gone by after Mary's return from
school when her father at the dinner-table one day looked
round with a chuckle and said, 'You'll none of you guess
where I'm off to next.'

The family began to make wild suggestions, from China
to Peru, for they were accustomed to his sudden expeditions
to outlandish places. No one was right, so then they
guessed Truro, Penzance, and even Hayle, thinking he was
having a little joke.

'All of you wrong. I have to start next week for
Spain.'

Then there was a chorus of 'What are you going for?'
'How long will you be away? Won't it be very hot?' 'Are
you going in a boat?' (this last from little Joe). He waved
them all down with a shake of the head and a confession of
ignorance as to all the details, except that there were some
districts of Spain where they were hoping to strike copper,
and he was to go to report on the possibilities. Looking at
the letter in his hand he said that the districts named were
quite unknown to him, and he would read them out for the
instruction of the family, only he couldn't pronounce them.

'The only familiar name to me so far,' he added, 'is our
port of landing—Santánder.'

'Santandér, you mean, father; that's how it's pronounced.'

All eyes were turned to Mary, who had jumped up in her seat and was looking at her father with glowing eyes,

'Take me with you.'

The younger ones took this for one of Mary's ever-surprising jokes, and laughed gleefully. Her parents and William only pretended to laugh, thinking this was the best way to treat the idea. Tony looked at her anxiously. It was soon evident to all that no joke was intended, for she poured forth her cogent reasons for wanting to see Spain.

'It's an extremely foreign country, my dear,' put in Nancy.

'I can speak French like a native, mother; they said so at school, and French will take you anywhere in the world.'

'The world, perhaps,' said her father, 'but not up-country among peasants, where I shall have to go.'

'But I know a little Spanish too, because one day in Bath we had a Spanish visitor, and she taught us a lot of useful phrases, like "how much?" "how far?" and things like that.'

'No doubt, dear, and very nice too, but your going is quite out of the question.' There he should have stopped, but he added, 'Goodness knows what sort of travelling we shall have, on sea and land.'

'Pooh, father, that's nothing. I went out for a sail several times when I was at Falmouth, and was never sick.'

Every argument against her going was knocked down, for whatever else she had failed to learn at school, she had certainly learned to argue. However, the next day her father came home with a final objection. He had intended to take William with him, but now it was found to be necessary to leave him at home to attend to the management of one of the mines, and a clerk would have to go instead of him. Of course if William had been there to look after her it might have been possible, but he could never leave her in charge of a young clerk.

But Mary soon demolished the clerk obstacle. 'Nonsense, father dear. I don't want any looking after. It 's more likely that I shall be useful in looking after both you and the clerk. Which is to go? Tonkin?'

Her determination secretly delighted her father, and at this he exclaimed 'That's the spirit! Go you shall!'

Nancy's misgivings were not brought to the surface, for her husband had taught her never to let private worries damp an adventure. Tony was almost as excited as Mary, and the two sisters set about discussing what should be packed, and putting together all they could remember about Spain. They got out the huge family atlas, and tried to find the unpronounceable districts mentioned in the letter, but the old map of Spain was very reserved about them, and seemed to be almost as free from 'places' as Africa.

'I feel like a kind of Marco Polo,' said Mary, 'to return after many years quite unrecognizable.'

It was in the early spring when she and her father and the clerk set out by coach to Falmouth. Here there was a delay of a few days before their ship was to sail. The time was full enough of fun for Mary. In addition to the fascination of good shops and the general liveliness of the port, she had the excitement of a ball given by the naval officers stationed there. She had scoffed at Tony's insistence on her packing an evening gown. 'To please the natives, I suppose you think,' she had said. But Tony had replied, 'You never know, and it takes little room.' Now of course she was glad enough of it—a simple black dress, of the finest soft silk, cut very low, showing up her white neck and shoulders.

They arrived late at the ball, and Mary was vaguely aware that their entrance made a little sensation. As usual, she thought, father seems king of his company. Her first dance was with a distinguished-looking young officer named Symons. He danced to perfection, but was rather stiff in the conversation line, so after the usual remarks on the state of the floor and the music, she gave herself up to enjoying one of the best dances she had ever had. She was a little surprised at the end that her partner suggested sitting out the next dance, and conducted her to a quiet corner. She wondered what she could possibly talk about, but in the meantime he had thought up something to say, and inquired brightly how long her stay in Falmouth was to be. This was a legitimate question, and she seized the chance to tell him merrily of her father's errand to Spain, and the reason, or lack of it, of her own part in the venture, with the Marco Polo motif running through her account.

'It is appropriate that you should go South,' said he. 'Do you know, when I saw you come into the room I thought you were an Italian princess?'

'In disguise, I suppose? It isn't the first time I've been taken for an Italian. I used to boast at school that I was descended from an early Roman invader. My name Vivian lent colour to the legend.'

'Oh, I didn't catch the name when I was introduced. I'm too good a Cornishman not to know that name well.' With a flush and some hesitation he added, 'Have you by any chance any other name?'

'A most unusual one—Mary. I hope you can produce something equally staggering?'

'Mine's John—a fitting match to yours.'

They both laughed, and Mary went on hurriedly, 'Now I've told you where I'm going. It's your turn to tell me where you are expecting to be next.'

'We are off in a week or so to the West Indies, and shall probably be stationed for some time in the Bermudas.'

'How exciting! I wonder whether you will find them still vexed.'

'Oh, you read Shakespeare!' Their talk after this became a delighted comparison of their favourite plays and poems. They were quite lost to their surroundings until Cap'n Vivian appeared with an elder officer, to take Mary off for a dance.

'I'll leave you here, father, to have a chat with my late partner. Lucky man, he is going to the Bermudas.'

The chat ended in a cordial invitation to the young officer to spend his next leave, or as much of it as he could spare, with the Vivian family at Reskadinnick, 'among the tin mines'.

'It may be some time, Sir, before I am back in England, but you may be sure that I shall pay my respects to you before doing anything else.'

§ 2

John Symons had talked enthusiastically about the poetry of a sailing vessel—the beautiful curves, the graceful dips,

the exhilaration given by the movement, the music of the
incidental sounds made by the winds, the waves and the
'works', quoting freely from the *Ancient Mariner*, and from
an address to the ocean by Byron. Even so Mary was not
prepared for the immense pleasure she found in the first
part of her voyage. Her father's sea stories, John's quota-
tions, and the novelty of the surroundings, all combined
to enchant her. But for a few hours in the Bay she wished
she hadn't come. Deadly ill, she lay down in her little bunk,
clutching the edge and saying to herself, 'I've brought it on
myself, this awful trip, and I'll get through it somehow.'
Presently she remembered John's remark when she asked
him what became of the poetry when there were heavy seas
running. 'It's more poetical than ever,' he had said, 'the
mistake people make is to fight against the motion of the
vessel, trying to keep themselves straight; the thing to do
is to *give* to its every sway, just as you move with a horse.'
So with an invitation to the vessel to take her anywhere it
fancied, she fell asleep, to be wakened by her father saying,
'Here's Santander, Mary. Come along.'

Dry land of any kind would have been welcome, but the
lovely harbour that met her eyes compensated for all she
had been through. Setting foot for the first time in a foreign
country must always stir the imagination, but here Mary's
wildest expectations were exceeded. The drive through the
streets in a rickety carriage gave promise of endless things
to explore. At every turn, and the streets were far from
straight, she glimpsed something that must be seen better
later—the rich colouring of the trappings of the carts, the
animals and the peasants in the market-place, and above

all the dazzling white tower of the cathedral making the sky an intenser blue than she had ever seen before.

In appearance the hotel was palatial, and to Mary was assigned the best bedroom, one in which they understood the proprietor to say Prince Charles of England had slept. Mary was duly impressed and began to hunt in her mind for the occasion and the exact prince. However royal in flavour, the place was a little lacking in ordinary appurtenances, and no chambermaid was to be found, nor any bell (that would work) to summon one. So after some hesitation Mary went up to a very tall man, obviously disengaged for the moment, for he was leaning against an ornate pillar. She could think of no operative word except the Italian *ritirata*, but it acted. The man inclined his head, beckoned her to follow and strode away with stately gait down a long corridor, and out into the grounds; presently he halted in front of a wooden door, flung it wide open and made a sweeping bow with the words, 'Be'ole, señorita.' Swallowing her desire to laugh, Mary thanked him with a curtsey, and entered with what dignity she could muster.

The following day she set out to explore the town while her father and his clerk were making inquiries about their route. As she sauntered along the streets and alleys she found it hard to realize that a people who went about all their business in such a placid fashion could ever have conquered South America or invented the Inquisition. A castle attracted her, and she ventured inside; there seemed to be nobody in charge of it, and presently she discovered an evil-looking stone cellar that might easily have been used as a dungeon. It brought to her mind the horrible story of the man in the days of the inquisition who was imprisoned in complete darkness; he trod round the wall to measure it; trod again to make sure and found it one pace less; trod again; again one pace less; always one pace less—a nightmare of a story. Hurrying back into the colourful streets once more she noticed that a people may be lazy and yet be cruel. She could hardly bear to see the way the horses were treated. Returning to the hotel to fetch her sketch-book, she found her father waiting for her on the steps.

'There'll be no time for sketching, I'm afraid. We must be off to-morrow morning. I find that we shall have to go everywhere on horse-back. Can you manage that?'

'Manage it! Why, if a Cornishman has one leg in the sea, he has the other over the back of a horse.'

'M—yes, but a Cornish horse. However, the chief point is that you must pack the very least possible, and leave all your main luggage here against we come back.'

This was the first time she had ever had to limit her luggage, and she found it an amusing exercise. The number of things she could do without was astonishing. Each article was held up and interrogated 'Now are you really necessary?' I am approximating, she thought, to the status of a tramp, and it isn't far removed from that of my ideal man of wealth who owns nothing, carries nothing, buys what he wants as he wants it, and leaves it behind him when done with. But one couldn't be really wealthy in Spain like that, for I expect there will be few shops where we are going. Few shops! She laughed a little later at this idea.

She had been accustomed, too, not only to take what clothes she fancied, but also the horse she liked best in the stable. It was a set-back therefore when she saw the Hobson's choice that was brought to the hotel entrance next morning.

'Is this one mine? Why, it is Rozinante resurrected—or nearly—your pardon, Rozinante!'

Her father praised her small pack and arranged it in the rear of the huge saddle, which was roomy indeed, and looked more comfortable than it turned out to be. But Rozinante made a better pace than was expected, and jogged along the rough paths, stumbling over little pits and stones, and recovering itself every time so adroitly that Mary let the reins pretty well alone. Her father and Tonkin were ahead leading the way, so there was no worry but to jog after them. She was heartily glad when a halt was called, and the little something by the wayside was said to be an inn. Three travellers were evidently an event, and there was quite a stir to prepare a meal. Mary was glad enough to stretch her legs a little as soon as she had seen Rozinante taken for a feed.

When they sat down to their 'dinner', 'What animal is this, father?' she asked.

'Goat, I think. But it is wiser not to ask or to think about it at all.'

'I'm more thirsty than hungry, and this light wine is just the thing.'

What she mostly regretted was not having squeezed into her pack some kind of sketching things. This so-called inn was quite indescribable in words, but its ramshackle state would have made an attractive drawing. However, they had to push on almost at once, and rode till sundown, when they reached a larger inn, where they were to spend the night. This was a more imposing building than the way-side shanty, and Mary was pleased at the thought of a bath, for she was a pale yellow from head to foot with dust. 'A bath!' the idea was almost as funny as the 'few shops'.

'Ask the man to show me my room,' she said to her father.

'My dear,' he replied, 'I don't know what you'll say, but there *are* no bedrooms. Just come and look here.'

The meal was laid in a kind of large verandah, and behind this was the roofed-in part of the building. This consisted of one big room, with couches arranged round the sides. In one corner stood a table with a basin and a pitcher of water.

'This is the guest-room,' said her father, 'and where the innkeeper and his servants sleep I have not cared to inquire. Whatever will you do?'

'Why, do as the Spaniards do, of course. We can at all events lie down, and I'm so stiff that the mere lying down will be a luxury.'

Either she was very hungry or the food was better, for she enjoyed the dinner in the cool of the evening, with the after-glow of the sunset streaming in on the candle-lit table. She enjoyed watching the deft movements of the brightly dressed girls who waited on them, and listening to the dignified tones of the innkeeper who was apparently praising the wine that he was bringing to them.

After spending a night of complete indifference to her surroundings, she next morning waylaid one of the servants and succeeded in making her understand that she wanted some 'food for three' to take with them. A promising-looking basket was hung on her saddle as they were starting off, and after they had ridden three or four hours, she hailed her father, 'We needn't look for an inn to-day. I've brought a picnic.'

While they were tying up the horses, she laid out the contents of her basket. She found fruit and cheese and eggs, with some rolls and a small bottle of wine. These she laid out on a flat stone in as pleasant a way as she could, but was troubled at the absence of glasses.

'That's all right,' said her father. 'We can use the cup of my flask.'

They voted it the best meal they had had since they had left the boat. So this plan was carried out nearly every day, much to Cap'n Vivian's satisfaction, for it left him free for his investigating journeys up-country, where inns were extremely rare. Occasionally an inn where they put up for the night had a more elaborate guest-room, with curtains separating the beds, in a kind of cubicle plan. Then they had a chance for a change of raiment, and (after urgent demands for water) something of a wash. One day Cap'n Vivian came in to the evening meal with 'Who do you think is working in a mine here, Mary?'

'Some one from home?'

'Yes, Peter Toy, of Trelowarren. I heard a Cornish voice and hailed it. You should have heard his delighted "*Thee* is it, Cap'n Vivian!"'

'I expect he's horribly homesick,' said Mary.

'Does that mean that *you* are, little woman?'

'Oh no, father, I'm enjoying every bit of the time, and am getting used to the long rides, and quite fond of Rozinante. But what I do long for is a bit of plain bread and butter.'

At this the innkeeper was summoned, and every effort put forth to make him understand what butter was. Mary drew a cow, showed milk flowing from its udder, made movements as of beating cream and a gesture as of spreading on a piece of bread. The man called his daughter, and they both talked excitedly in Spanish for a bit. Then the girl disappeared and returned with butter for the señorita—in a bottle!

'Never mind, Mary, we shall be having our Cornish butter soon. I've got just one more district to reach and make a report on, and then we head for the coast. According to all accounts it is a pretty wild region, farther from civilization than any we have been to yet. So be prepared for roughing it.'

'The rougher the merrier! I'm well broken in, and I should like something really out-and-out Spanish to happen, to tell Tony when we get back.'

'I should have thought you had had enough.'

'She and I read some of *Don Quixote* before I started, and we came to one scene in an inn that really, father, was so disgusting that we had to put the book away.'

'Well, dear, if you are hoping for that kind of thing we shall be sure to find something satisfactory, if indeed we find an inn at all.'

Cap'n Vivian had made out from his instructions a rough map of their route, which led through a hilly district where the possible mines were to be prospected, and then led on to Santander. The road was definitely rougher than any they had been on before, and at one point Cap'n Vivian called back that he feared the horses wouldn't be able to get through the next bit.

'Is there any other way round?' asked Mary.

'I don't see any chance. Tonkin and I could walk through, but we can't leave you here. We must simply go back to where we left the main road, and I must give up this bit of prospecting.'

'That is the last thing we must do,' said Mary. 'Let us have our lunch, rest the horses, and think out what we can manage.'

After this refreshing interval she suggested that they two should have a quiet smoke, while she could climb up a rock that overhung the path a little farther on, and have a look at the prospect. She returned with the news that she thought Rozinante could manage to get through, and the other horses would probably follow. She had also seen two men hanging over a rock a longish way ahead, but as soon as they sighted her they disappeared.

'Then there are some people about,' said her father hopefully, 'so there is sure to be an inn of some kind within reasonable reach before nightfall. Let's have a try to get through.'

Rozinante was undoubtedly the best horse, but Cap'n Vivian insisted on riding it himself to lead the way, as he didn't like the idea of men leaning over rocks and watching them. It might be all right, but if any little game was on foot, he didn't want Mary to be in front.

'Nor you either, Tonkin,' he added; 'I've done some fighting in my time, you know, and can cope with these foreign fellows. They usually run away if you shake a stick at them,' and he twirled his big stick merrily round his head before stowing it by Rozinante's saddle.

So they set off in the order named. But very soon Rozinante jibbed, in spite of all Cap'n Vivian's encouraging noises and well-directed smacks and kicks. Most unusual with him, annoyance set in—increased by the sound of Mary's laughter behind.

'It's no use, we shall have to go back, but it's nothing to laugh at,' and a few stronger words followed addressed to the horse.

'Let me have a try,' said Mary, 'I think a bit of a jump would do it,' and amid many expostulations she induced her father to let her mount Rozinante again and lead the way. She took her time, talked to the horse, patted him, gave him a piece of sugar, and ordered the little cavalcade to go back some fifty yards, and turn. Then she started off at a brisk pace, gave the horse the right flick at the right moment, and over the worst of the rocky part he went in one bound. Then she pulled him up and encouraged him on before there was time to hesitate, and went ahead without looking back. When at last she was on steadier ground and ventured to pull up, she gave a cheer, for the others were coming on too.

'Well done, Mary!' cried her father, 'you're the sort for a tight place.'

After a few more miles of rather slow progress along the track, they came to a wider path, almost a road, which evidently was the one indicated on their plan.

'It's near here that our bit of prospecting lies,' said Cap'n Vivian, 'and if there's an inn anywhere to be found we can put up the horses and go up on foot.'

An inn there certainly was, but it outdid all the former ones in its lack of the things that make an inn attractive.

'Now I hope you are satisfied. This looks equal to anything you could have read about in *Don Quixote*.'

The interior was in accordance. The guest-room certainly had four couches on which lying down was possible, but for washing there seemed to be nothing but a pump in the yard. However, the stables were ample and well stocked for the horses, and Mary herself led Rozinante in for a well-deserved dinner. As soon as the travellers had eaten what they could of the meal provided, the two men went off on foot to their work, and Mary was left to sit in the verandah till they returned. She dozed a little, for the sleepiness of the place was infectious, then took a walk round to see the view, regretting for the hundredth time that she had not brought her sketch-book. Especially when she saw a man just like those who had been hanging over the roadway—an enormously tall, sinister-looking fellow, in knee-breeches with a fantastic scarf of every colour thrown over his shoulders, and a long knife in his belt. 'What a lovely brigand! And to think that I can't draw him for Tony', thought she, as she watched him stride in, call for a drink and stop for a gossip with the landlord. Gossip it was, no doubt, although it sounded as if they were quarrelling. But all foreigners sounded as if they were quarrelling, she reflected, and perhaps they were really in complete agreement on the ghastly heat of the weather.

Cap'n Vivian returned at sundown, rubbing his hands at having made a very promising survey.

'The best I have had so far. I wouldn't have missed it for anything. And it's all your doing, Mary,' and he called for a bottle of the best wine that the house could produce.

After supper the innkeeper was consulted as to the right road for Santander, and fortunately it led straight on, so that there would be no need to go back over the rough road. And if they made a good pace they might reach the port in two days. They lay down for the night fully clothed, with the pleasant thought that this would be the last of the kind, that on the following night they would be somewhere civilized enough to give them a chance for a wash and a change.

Soon there was a sound in the outer place as of late customers coming in, of drinks being served, of laughter and talking, but they were all too sleepy to pay much attention to it. Mary half woke, thought 'foreigners quarrelling again I suppose', and fell asleep. After she had been asleep for what seemed to her many hours she was awakened by her father putting his hand gently over her mouth to prevent a sudden exclamation. He then whispered to her that they were in great danger. The innkeeper had crept in to tell him that a gang of nearly twenty banditti were lying on the floor in the outer place. They had got news of a rich Englishman and his daughter travelling in the neighbourhood. They had been spying about during the day, trying to get information from him, and now they had come in force. The words 'daughter' and 'ransom' were repeated so often that there was little doubt as to their main idea. The innkeeper had shown considerable sense. Instead of denying the presence of his guests or their money, as he had tried to do at first, he changed his tactics and encouraged the enterprise with promise of great spoil. On the strength of this he stood drinks all round. And now they were all dead drunk.

Such particulars Cap'n Vivian pieced together from the excited words and gestures of the innkeeper. The only point that he put to Mary at the moment was that the robbers were lying drunk, there was no time to lose, they must step through them, and make for their horses, which the innkeeper had tethered close at hand, ready for them. Mary nodded her comprehension, and then Tonkin was roused in the same way. Cap'n Vivian led, and Mary followed, too excited to be frightened. The banditti were rather an alarming sight——huge fellows, all dressed in the style she had been admiring in the afternoon, but not so picturesque as they lay there snoring. By the side of each was a gleaming knife, within reach, ready for action. She gathered up her skirt, and stepped more gingerly than she had ever stepped before, taking care to plant her foot each time close to one of the knives. If one of the men should show signs of waking she knew who would seize the knife first.

Meanwhile her father had got safely through and was pushing gold into the innkeeper's hand. He used to say that he had never left an hotel tipping so heavily or so willingly. Handing Mary on to her horse, and telling her to gallop off at once, he turned round to wait for his clerk. The poor young fellow had hurried too much and had trodden too near the last man and roused him. Fortunately the robber was too stupefied to do more than seize his knife and with a badly aimed lunge make a slight flesh wound in Tonkin's leg. No time to bother about it, and the two men mounted their horses as quietly as possible and made off after Mary. She had halted after going hard for a quarter of a mile or so, and was relieved to see them coming on, and to hear her father's cheery voice, 'No fear of their catching us now, Mary,' and as they drew close, 'that noble inn-keeper gave me to understand that he would put them on the wrong track. But see whether you can bandage a wound. Tonkin here had a taste of one of those knives.'

The clerk was laid on the ground, while Mary searched her pack for some clean handkerchiefs to tear into strips. Her father produced his emergency bottle of water, and a fair job was soon made of the wound. While he was pouring out a nip from his brandy flask—'finest thing for a wounded man'—Mary told Tonkin to raise himself up by putting his arms round her shoulders. This he did with just a shade too much *empressement*. Smiling to herself she said, 'Pull as hard as you like, you won't hurt me.'

They reached Santander without further mishap, and Mary had never rejoiced in a bedroom so much as she did in her Prince Charles's one, where her trunks were awaiting her return. The two days in the port before they sailed were sheer delight, spent in sketching and shopping. Among the many gifts for everybody that she accumulated were two figures, over twelve inches high, representing bandits. These were brightly coloured, and would show them at home the kind of ruffian she had trodden over. Another of her spoils was a magnificent many-coloured heavy silk shawl. This had been bought chiefly to heighten the effect of a dance she had watched the peasants executing in the market-place. She managed to memorize the air and the steps, and felt confident that she could put on the shawl and do it at home to amuse the children.

Their home port on return was Falmouth, and although
Mary had been sorry to leave Spain, her heart warmed at
the sight of the Cornish coast again. In the hotel where
they put up for the night a fresh interest arose. Just arrived
in his own vessel was a business friend of Cap'n Vivian's,
a Norwegian timber-merchant named Barnholt. For this
man he had come to feel not only respect, but real affection.
With him were his two daughters, Yetta and Sophie, who
at once fraternized with Mary.

'I brought them over in my boat,' said he, 'to see a bit of
London while we were discharging in the Thames, and in
two days we shall be off to Norway again.'

'What good fortune that we met you. Can't you spare
a few days to run down to see my wife?'

'Impossible, I must get back to the mills at once.'

'How absurd,' broke in Mary, 'to snatch your daughters
away with you, before they have seen anything. Can't they
come down to stay for a bit with us at Reskadinnick, father?'

'That is a very kind thought,' replied Mr. Barnholt, 'but
it may be a year before I come to England again.'

'And do you suppose,' said Cap'n Vivian, 'that the
interest of Cornwall can be exhausted in a year?'

Then followed a warm invitation to Reskadinnick for as
long as they could, and a delighted acceptance by the girls.
The surprise arrival at home with the increased family was
one of Mary's jolliest recollections. A visit of many months
or even a year was by no means unusual in those days, and
Mrs. Vivian was always able to get bedrooms ready at a
minute's notice. What with the unpacking of gifts and telling
of adventures and the mighty supper, at which the children

were allowed to sit up, Reskadinnick was at the top of its form.

As usual, Mary and Tony had a private chat after the family had said good-night.

'Father seems to have had a successful time,' said Tony.

'Yes, he is full of the report he is going to make of what can be done in one or two districts we visited. And of course he was pressing on every educated man we met in Santander the grand scope there is for a railway from the port to Madrid.'

'He seems to care as much about railways as mines. I suppose he talked about Andrew Vivian and Trevithick and all the Cornish had done?'

'Yes, and the Spaniards listened with polite interest, but I didn't think they looked like starting anything.'

'Could father make himself understood?'

'Pretty well, mostly in French, and I was able to help him out now and again.'

'From what you told us at supper I guess you never had a chance to wear your evening frock?'

'Oh but I did, Tony, with great effect, for we had a glorious ball given by the naval officers in Falmouth.'

'Did you dance with any one special?'

'With one or two of the high and mighty ones—very correct and stately, but practically dumb.'

'No one worth remembering?'

'There was one young officer, a first-lieutenant, a Cornish-man named John Symons, at present on H.M.Brig *Ranger*. He is off to the West Indies by now. His home is in Falmouth, and——'

'Hullo, Mary,' laughed Tony, 'you seem to have found out a good deal about him. A bit struck, were you?'

Mary coloured, and for the first time Tony saw how attractive she had become. But her sisterly hope for a bit of romance was a little dashed by Mary's next words, 'Yes, a little, Tony, I certainly was, and I think he was rather involved too. But he quoted a few lines of "La Belle Dame" —beautifully, you know, but just a shade too sentimentally —and I wanted to laugh.'

'Oh, that's nothing. It's only a young man's ardour. Think of all our acquaintances about here who have never heard so much as whether there *be* a Keats.'

'True, but still——Anyhow, father has asked him to come here to stay when he gets his next leave.'

'That's good,' said Tony, who felt that there was more in it than Mary chose to admit.

'One thing I am determined—that I do not go for any trip again unless you come too.'

THREE

OTTO

§ 1

MARY had tasted blood in going abroad, but had to wait some time for her next chance. Greenland was the scene of her father's prospecting shortly after the Spanish one, but even Mary was daunted by the look of the map—so cold and entirely bare of 'places'. William went off with his father without a protest from her. And in any case it would not have done to leave her guests—the two Barnholt girls.

Yetta and Sophie came in age between Mary and Tony, and the four girls between them relieved Nancy of much of the work of the house, while she was occupied with the baby girl, Fan. Mary's main job, after her expensive education, was obviously to teach the others. Nicholas had been sent away to school, but there were Lizzie, Joe, and Emily to be taken seriously every morning. Tony became proficient in the direction of food-supply—no light task for such a big family. And the two Barnholt girls lent a hand wherever it was needed. To Nancy's pleasure and to Mary's incredulity Yetta professed a positive passion for mending, and was always in the middle of patching a sheet or making a shirt look like new. Sophie was an adept at music, and taught Tony how to read it. Very soon none of them could play so well as Tony, for she had a quite extraordinary lightness of touch and sense of rhythm. Ability to draw she had picked up from sheer love of the trees and animals around her. Her brother Nicholas had taught her how to manage an accident or ailment in cattle or chicken. He was intending to be a doctor, and was all for healing everything he could lay hands on. Her brother Joe's interest lay in quite another direction, since he was for making wounds rather than mending them. The Navy—that was his dream. Although only about ten years old, he had picked up (in that strange way that boys do) all the main technical lore about managing a vessel, and insisted on instructing Tony whether she wanted or not. He found a ready listener in Sophie, whom he adored. She would hold him entranced with stories of the Vikings and the navigation of the fjords.

The recreation time of the four girls was varied enough—riding, walking, sketching, picnics with the children, dances, and musical evenings—there was always something to do. A wet day they often spent reading Shakespeare together in parts. One day Mary suggested that they should dress up a bit and act some scenes from *A Midsummer Night's Dream* to the children in lesson-time. The others were shocked. To read a play, or listen to it, when they ought to be doing sums! But Mary had her way, offering some absurd argument about a knowledge of literature: 'I've taught them when Shakespeare was born and died and all that. It can't hurt them to read or hear a bit of him.'

Wanting another grown-up to take a part, they asked a girl in Camborne to join them. Mary was astonished at her knowledge of the play.

'You seem to have read *A Midsummer Night's Dream* before?'

'Yes,' replied the girl. 'Mother told me on no account to read Shakespeare, because he is so gross. So of course I read a lot of the plays on the quiet, to see what the gross bits were.'

'And I trust you were successful?' asked Mary.

'No. I couldn't find a single thing.'

Mary smothered her laughter and suggested that the mother must have been mistaken, thinking of some other dramatist no doubt.

What struck the Norwegian girls more than anything else in Cornwall was the mildness of the winter and the rarity of snow. 'You should see,' they said, 'our ski-ing in Norway. You Cornish people are too soft.' But a cliff walk or two in the teeth of a sou'-wester soon made them see another side to it. However, Christmas seemed to them odd without skating and tobogganing, and the religious rites were tame compared to the Norwegian. The description of these aroused Tony's curiosity.

§ 2

Every member of the family was dismayed when a letter arrived in the following Spring to say that Mr. Barnholt's ship the *Skien,* was due to dock in the Thames in a fortnight, and Yetta and Sophie must be ready to return to Norway in her. After many warm expressions of politeness and gratitude for hospitality, the letter ended with an earnest hope that any members of Mrs. Vivian's family who cared to come for a visit to Norway would avail themselves of the returning vessel.

'How kind of Mr. Barnholt! Quite out of the question,

of course,' was Nancy's comment as she finished reading the letter aloud in the front kitchen, where every one had gathered to hear it.

But Yetta and Sophie burst in with other views. Or rather determinations. Yetta refused to start without taking Mary with her, and Sophie wouldn't go without Tony. Up and down they were discussing the point and urging endless reasons, when a little voice broke in, 'Does the letter say "any", mother?'

It was Joe, trying to peep at the letter. Tony saw his eyes shining with excitement, and that settled her own mind.

'We'll manage to go somehow, mother, and take Joe with us.'

This decision was hailed with acclamation by the Barnholts, and Mary followed up with: 'Yes, he's been a very good boy over his lessons, and deserves a holiday. I can set Lizzie and Emily some work to do and they can teach little Fan her letters against we come back.'

'But won't it be too big a party for Mrs. Barnholt?' asked Nancy.

The Barnholts were amused at such an idea. It seemed they had an enormous house, capable of putting up any number of guests, 'and dear little Joe', put in Sophie, 'shall have his fill of sailing on the fjords'.

Then followed a furious time of surveying of wardrobes and packing of trunks by the girls, and an intensive study of his *Nautical Guide* by Joe—everything delayed by the endless questions and offers of help from the little girls. On one of these busy days baby Fan was lost for an hour or two, and finally discovered fast asleep in Tony's half-packed trunk. From her confused babblings it was gathered that she had intended to 'go Norby too'.

It was an evening in a mid-April of the forties when the four girls and all their luggage were packed into the carriage, and Sammy, now head coachman, with Joe seated beside him, drove them off, amid endless blessings and warnings, to Hayle. Here they went aboard the steamship *Brilliant*, leaving the same evening for Bristol. It was as well they had a good night on the boat, for Tony was almost as excited as Joe over a first experience of travelling in a train. Mary pretended to be blasée with any form of transport, but she enjoyed the quick run to London on the Great Western as much as they did.

Rooms had been taken for them in Lambeth until the ship should be ready, and the interval of waiting was spent in exploring London. They paid a visit to the Surrey Zoological Gardens and were vastly amused with the animals, especially the monkeys. Mary thought to improve the occasion by pointing out to Joe that a monkey had four hands, when suddenly the monkey under observation offered a convincing proof of her remarks by snatching her hat and throwing it to the entire cage for sport, where it was soon in shreds. Mary was as tickled as the other visitors at the absurd end to her lesson, but Tony said, 'What are we to do? You can't go about like that.'

'Why, take a cab to the nearest hat-shop, of course—a good excuse for a new one. No, not the nearest shop, we'll go to Regent Street and get a good one.'

A visit to St. James's Park, and watching the Life Guards

at Buckingham Palace, took up most of another day. A
ride in a goat-chaise was exciting for Joe, but nothing to
touch his intoxication on the third day when a letter arrived
to say they were to come aboard. 'Orders to embark,' said
Tony; 'isn't that music, Joe?'

A primitive kind of railway, where the train was worked
by a rope, took them from Fenchurch Street to Blackwall.
Here the terminus was quite an imposing building (and is
still standing). It was dark when they reached the dock,
but out of the darkness came a call in Norsk 'Are you there?'
and in answer to Yetta's reply there stepped up to them the
second mate of the *Skien*. He had a boat waiting to take
them alongside. The cargo had been discharged, a small
amount of ballast taken in, and the vessel was moored out in
the river, ready to drop down with the morning ebb. As
they all climbed up the ship's ladder they were heartily
greeted by Captain Christian Barnholt, the girls' uncle, a
Norwegian of commanding presence, built on a magnificent
scale.

Joe felt himself to be a real sailor at last, as he crept into
his bunk for the night. To his chagrin he overslept, woke
to find it broad daylight, that he had missed the start, and
that they were already some way down the Thames. Trying
to make up for lost time he took in all he could of the surrounding shipping, and was soon absorbed in the progress
of a brig going down close to them. When at last she was
left astern he shouted to his sisters who were getting letters
ready for the pilot, 'Tell mother that we've beat the *Betsy*.'
By dusk they were off Gravesend, past the lightships, and
making for the North Sea with a fair wind.

In the next three days the wind dropped and they were so becalmed on the Dogger Bank that nearly all hands had their fishing-lines over the side, and a great quantity of cod was hauled in. Captain Barnholt was quite fretful because there was no hake caught.

'Why the worry?' asked Mary. 'Isn't cod good enough?'

'Far too good for the crew, that's the matter.'

Then followed four days of very slow progress, as the vessel with her small ballast lazily rolled along. The girls stood it fairly well, but poor little Joe was so ill that he had to be given brandy. They were all glad to hear the cry 'Land on the port bow'.

This was the Naze, and Norway at last. When they dropped anchor at Brevig a boat came off shore bringing new milk and delicious newly baked rye cakes. Joe had been unable to touch food for two days, and a grateful memory of that meal remained with him all his life. Mary's chief memory of that arrival was the long row up the fjord to Skien, its broad peaceful waters, and the sunlight catching the barks of the birch-trees on the cliffs; all the trees and shrubs were at that magic stage when they were just bursting into leaf.

Tony's outstanding memory was of their young host, Otto. His sisters had talked a great deal about him, in such a way that Mary and Tony had feared he might turn out to be oppressively worthy. That idea was soon dispelled by the boyish warmth of his welcome to them at Brevig. And Tony noticed with gratitude on their row up the fjord how the colour was coming back to Joe's cheeks as Otto talked and laughed with him. Yetta and Sophie seemed to turn to their brother for everything, although he was the youngest of the family.

'How pleased my mother will be,' said he, 'to have a boy about the place again.'

§ 3

The home of the Barnholts was a large house facing the fjord. Between the river above and the fjord beneath rushed down a mighty fall. This was used to drive the wheels of a number of saw-mills that shaped the logs to be loaded on to the shipping lying alongside the wharves of the fjord. Mary and Tony were nearly deafened at first by the rattle of the mills, and were surprised that Yetta and Sophie didn't seem to hear it all.

As for their reception in this beautiful spot which was to be a second home to them for many months, they agreed that Mrs. Barnholt exceeded if possible the hospitable graces of their own mother. Most courteous of all was her extreme pleasure at the quite unexpected presence of little Joe. She brought out to amuse him the illustrated books and toy ships that she had kept since Otto's childhood. She sent a message inviting a neighbour to come up as often as possible to play with him, show him everything, and teach him some Norsk. A better companion could not have been found for Joe than this Theodore Theiste, who duly appeared next morning and eventually became a lifelong friend. He was as crazy about the sea as Joe, and knew much more about it practically, for he was two or three years older, and had learnt to navigate the fjord and indeed had almost lived in boats. Together they plotted happy futures, Joe in the Navy and Theo in the Merchant service.

Unfortunately for the visitors' progress in Norsk, every educated person they met could speak English. Mary might easily have used her facility in picking up languages for acquiring some Norsk, but she simply wouldn't be bothered, and these Northern languages she maintained were so uncouth after French. But Tony, perhaps because she had never been to school, grabbed at any kind of learning or acquirement; the Norsk words seemed to her to harmonize with the scenery and fascinated her. She found verse easy to pick up and committed a great deal to memory. The following quatrain Mary really did admire, more for its sound views on reticence and confidants than for its poetry, and she induced Tony to inscribe it in her album:

> Välg ikke til Fortrolig enhver som vil;
> Tomt Huus staar gjerne aabent, rigt lukket til.
> Välg een, unödigt er det paa Jo at lide;
> Og verden veed, o Halfdan! hvad Frende vide.

Don't make a confidant of every one who wants,
For an empty house is kept open, a rich one closed.
Choose one; *there is no need to rely on two;*
And the world knows, O Halfdan, what the neighbours know.

Tony would go out into the timber-yard to listen to Otto speaking to the men and pick up his phrases. She begged him one day to let her give a message for him to one of them. To her great pride the man understood and carried out the instructions. The only Norsk words that Mary picked up were, 'Er de gal, Marie?' This oft-repeated request from Otto to know if she were mad came from her rash exploits and impish pranks.

On the fourth morning of their stay Tony was awakened early—not by a strange noise, but by a strange silence. It alarmed her, and she ran to Sophie's room to ask what the unearthly quiet meant—was somebody dead?

'No, it's only Sunday,' laughed Sophie, 'when the mills always stop working.'

'I've never heard such a deep silence in my life,' said Tony.

Hastily dressing she ran outside to revel in this new beauty, and found that some other sounds were getting a chance, for neither the waterfall nor the birds nor the lambs knew anything of Sunday and were letting themselves go. After breakfast, of course, came the preparations for church-going. In Mr. Barnholt's case these were peculiar, and Joe watched his movements wide-eyed. He was a great smoker, nearly always 'anchored to a pipe' as he called it. On the wall of the dining-room hung his pipe-rack, containing many varieties. He went up to the rack and selected one with a stem some fifteen inches long, and a bowl as big as a tea-cup. This he filled with tobacco and put in his pocket. Seeing Joe's interest he said, 'May I have the pleasure of your company to church?'

Dazed with the honour, Joe started off beside him and saw how all the neighbourhood had decked themselves out in their best clothes, so different from the everyday ones, and were making for the church. Mr. Barnholt took Joe up the stairs to the gallery and into his own box, which was as private as a box in a theatre. Here he stood up and bowed to all his friends below, then lit his pipe and smoked in peace throughout the entire service. Joe was free to lean over and use his eyes, and there was plenty to look at beside his relations and friends in the pews below. Down there his sisters were being puzzled by the conduct of the service. It was a mixture of Catholic ritual and extreme Protestantism. The parson wore a black gown with a frill of Elizabethan pattern, reminding them of the picture of John Knox preaching to Mary Queen of Scots, while a pre-Lutheran note was introduced in the ceremony of Baptism. A baby near the font, wailing at intervals, had aroused Joe's expectations, but these were exceeded when a cherub was let down at the critical moment from the ceiling, holding a gilded bowl filled with holy water straight from heaven.

Another medieval note was the behaviour of the community as soon as the service was over. The religious duty performed, all the rest of the day was given up wholeheartedly to rest or recreation. There was nothing of the puritanical Sunday, with nearly every enjoyment forbidden.

'Why can't Cornwall be like this?' said Mary. 'I suppose we've Wesley to thank for our dire Sundays.'

'Mother would never allow us to do this kind of thing. "Popery, my dear," she would say. We had better not mention it in our letters.'

'This kind of thing' included open-air dancing and sports. The music was of a very lively kind, and the dancing graceful but vigorous. A young Norse girl induced Joe to join her in a round, but he was overcome with shyness and soon wriggled away, and much preferred to watch several young peasants climbing a greasy pole to gain the leg of mutton at the top. To his great indignation, the boy who won it had secreted sand in his pocket.

During the first two months of their visit the four girls

went about a great deal by themselves. Household duties occupied their hostess and business ones their host. Otto snatched a day for an excursion whenever he could, but that was not very often. Mary and Tony were perfectly happy wandering about the countryside, attempting to sketch the impossible mountains, streams, and trees just coming into full foliage. They were astonished at the immediate attention and deference shown them as soon as the name Barnholt was mentioned. It was a password for anything that they wanted—meals, transport of every kind on land or fjord, messages, flowers, fruit, milk, and above all, the immediate smiles of welcome. No smallest coin would even a child accept; and Mary tried her hardest.

Almost the best part of the day was after supper, when the chill of early summer evenings made the log fire in the great dining-room a welcome centre. Then they played chess, or studied Norsk legends, or showed the sketches they had done. Mary destroyed most of hers, disgusted with the way they fell short of what she wanted, but Tony's sketch-book was preserved, for it made a kind of diary of this blissful period of her life. Every tree or house or boat or mountain she drew with scrupulous care. For Tony was in love with Norway—she was in love with Otto. When that love-story began no one knew—certainly not Otto and Tony themselves. It seemed as if it had always been, and that when Tony first came to Norway it was not as a stranger. While Mary regarded the visit as a charming episode in a life full of experiment and adventure, Tony found in it a deep and complete satisfaction for all the vague poetical dreams of her girlhood.

After many evenings spent in reading about the ancient customs and folk-lore of Scandinavia, and telling the girls of his hope of the revival of them, Otto decided that they must plan a big expedition into the Telemarken hinterland.

'Up there,' said he, 'the old costumes are still worn, the old dances kept up, and the old tales, songs, and music can still be heard. We'll go there, Tony, and you will be able to dig out your folk-lore at first hand. But we must wait till full summer to see the country there in perfection.'

Meanwhile Joe and Theodore were pursuing their own ends, and if his boy companion couldn't come Joe could rely on Mary to join him in some fresh adventure. One day, with the aid of an old fisherman, these two managed to bring home enough whiting to make a dish for the family supper. Mrs. Barnholt allowed them to clean and cook the fish themselves, to the great amusement of the kitchen staff.

Joe had a standing invitation to go up to the house of Captain Christian Barnholt, to see the models of ships and treasures from all lands that he had collected, and to hear an occasional yarn in connexion with them. Over the mantel-piece was a large oil-painting that had a peculiar fascination for Joe. It depicted a large vessel that had lost most of its masts and rigging, sailors at one or two guns, and right in the middle a short stout man in the act of shooting another.

One afternoon when Captain Christian seemed in a coming-on disposition Joe ventured to ask him what it was all about, and why there should be a special picture of the shooting of one of the enemy.

'Ah, that's the point. The man being shot isn't an enemy. The captain is shooting one of his own crew.'

'That seems a funny thing to do. Because he looks to have very few men left.'

'In a fight it isn't so much the number that counts but the kind of men you've got. Things were touch and go, for they were in the middle of one of the most exciting sea-fights ever known.'

'More important than Nelson's?' asked Joe.

'Not more important in result, but more uncertain and exciting in the actual fighting. This captain here is the famous Paul Jones. He was what you call an adventurer, an able sailor who was ready for anything—almost a pirate in his way. Although I believe he was a Scot by birth, he helped the Americans against your country at the time when the Colonies were struggling for freedom. We ourselves here, and France and Holland, all felt great sympathy with them, but Paul Jones didn't stop at mere sympathy. It was just the kind of chance he liked. He knew the coasts of the British Isles well, and he made continual small raids on Ireland and Scotland, destroying ships and seizing goods, and was planning a big raid on England. The coast towns in the North were kept in a state of continual alarm.'

'That was fun,' said Joe.

'Yes, no doubt he got a great deal of fun out of it, and gain too, holding up and plundering any merchant-ship that struck his fancy. And I think the French enjoyed the joke quite as much; their vessels hung around, I tell you. Well, one September evening Paul Jones, in his lumbering old vessel the *Bonhomme Richard*, was making south for Flamborough Head when he sighted the Baltic fleet of merchant-men approaching the Humber, under convoy of a British man-of-war, H.M.S. *Serapis*. What did Jones do but stand up to the *Serapis* and open fire!'

'Ooh,' said Joe, 'I do hope he won.'

'Wait a bit. Of course the *Serapis* was a better-built ship for action, and had more guns, and very soon reduced the *Richard* to the almost total wreck you see in the picture. But Jones spied a French ship, the *Alliance*, a friend he had been hoping for, coming up to help him. So he took heart and encouraged his men to keep up the fight. What was their amazement to find this French ally, whose captain must have been drunk or mad, pouring a broadside into the *Richard*, instead of into the *Serapis*.

'That finished them, I suppose,' said Joe ruefully.

'No, it merely enraged Paul Jones, who at once started a new plan of attack. Of course Pearson, the captain of the *Serapis*, was just expecting his surrender every moment, and so were the crowd on the Yorkshire coast, who were watching the fight. One of Paul's crew was so certain of it that he ran up to haul down the flag himself. Now we come to the moment of the picture. Paul saw the man just in time and shot him out of hand.'

'And killed him, I hope. What happened then? Did Paul do his plan?'

'Oh yes. He had noticed a hole in the hatch of the *Serapis*, so he ordered a young middy to lie along the main yard and try to drop a grenade into this hole. The men kept handing up grenades to the boy who at last aimed one in, touching off a powder store. The starboard guns of the *Serapis* were wrecked and down came the mainmast. Now would you believe it, at this moment Pearson surrendered!'

'Whatever for? How absurd!' exclaimed Joe.

'The end of the story was still more absurd. Paul Jones and his men boarded the *Serapis* to take her over as a prize, and they had hardly done this when the old *Richard* sank. And funnier still, the *Serapis* was so badly injured that both crews working together had as much as they could do to keep her afloat as far as Holland. The English people were wild at one of their warships being surrendered to a pirate, and Paul Jones himself actually had to explain how well Pearson had fought before they could receive him decently. You see Paul fought so madly because he knew that he and all his men, if they surrendered, would be hanged as pirates.

'It was a middy, wasn't it, Sir, who really destroyed the *Serapis*?'

'Yes, and he too would have been hanged if he hadn't hit that hole. You must learn to aim accurately, my son.'

Joe's love of shooting had been encouraged in the timber-yard. When Theodore was unable to take him boating on the fjord, he spent nearly all his time in this paradise for a boy—a timber-yard with a knife. The workmen made him very welcome and showed quite an eagerness in helping him to make a fine bow and arrows, and to use them with good aim at various natural targets. Their foreman was a strict disciplinarian and thoroughly disliked by them all. He frowned even on the scraps of time they devoted to the education of Joe. One day he passed out of the office and was going across the yard just as Joe was standing idly by, scanning the view for a target. 'Have a shot at him,' said a voice at his elbow. Away went the arrow and struck the foreman full in the back. Protected as he was by a thick coat, he was more hurt in his dignity than in his back. But he had been forced to make an absurd jump, and finding that he had been frightened by a little boy (and that little time-waster, too) and that the men had laughed, he went fuming into the office to lodge a complaint. In the absence of Mr. Barnholt, Otto had to receive this. Quite as amused at the incident as the workmen, especially as it was described in passionate terms, Otto had to keep a straight face and summon Joe for a reprimand.

'Look here, my fine fellow,' he thundered out, 'do not slay my faithful men. Keep your fighting spirit for the Navy, and kill the enemies of your Queen,' knowing well that a reference to the Navy would sweeten the harshest scolding to Joe.

§ 4

At the end of July the weather was at its best, Otto was able to take a holiday, and all was in tune for the long-projected expedition up-country. As the Barnholt girls knew the valleys well they decided to stay at home with their parents, while Otto took the Cornish visitors. Theodore was invited to be a companion for Joe. By much studying of a big map hanging in the office, and much consultation with Yetta and Sophie, the girls found that most of the journey would be by water ('Hurrah!' said Joe, hovering around), and that the least possible luggage must be taken.

'Leave me alone for travelling light,' said Mary, and even the Barnholts were amazed at her packing ingenuity.

'I learnt to do this in Spain,' said she, with an off-hand air, as if her next hint would be about some idea she had picked up in Siberia.

Starting before sunrise, and that is very early in a Norwegian summer, the five explorers were driven in the Barnholt's carriage to the nearest point of the long lake which was to be their main line. The air was cold at first, but Otto said they would be shedding their wraps before long. As the mountains took on those mysterious colours of sunrise, so strangely unlike those of sunset and so much more inspiring, Mary muttered 'Not even rose-madder would be of any use.'

Her custom of turning everything she admired into terms of the colour-box was completely defeated here, so she fled to poetry and began spouting Coleridge's lines about the vale of Chamouny. But Tony objected: 'Sovran Blanc indeed! What can that neat little land-locked Switzerland be in comparison with our grand Norway?'

Otto had planned every bit of the route and ordered arrangements ahead, so that when they reached the lake a praam, one of the now familiar rowing-boats of the fjords, was waiting for them. In his eagerness to get in Joe nearly upset them all, and certainly this was the kind of travel best suited to the two boys. While the girls were in raptures over the new effects of the reflections of mountains and trees in the water, the boys were endeavouring to do a bit of fishing as they went. Mary stopped her poetical fancies, admitting 'even Keats would have been beaten here'. Tony appeared to be too happy to make any comment, and just pointed now and again with a deep intake of breath and a glance at Otto. He himself was smiling generally at the boatful of pleasure around him.

'Now, boys, for your appetites,' he cried, when they had gone some miles up the lake. Here was a cottage in which they were to have breakfast. While they were disembarking the boys spied a big cherry-tree, hanging over the lake, laden with crimson fruit, and they lost no time in climbing it. They were called in to breakfast with the warning that they were spoiling their appetites. But it takes more than a mere cherry-tree to spoil boys' zest for pancakes and honey, followed by relays of broiled ham, cured and cooked by a rosy-cheeked cottager.

Like giants refreshed with new wine, as Mary described the party, they took the praam again to the head of the lake where they were to spend the night. In the couple of hours of good daylight left Tony was able to do her first bit of research into manners. They went to visit the church and found abundant evidence of the old Catholic ritual untouched by Lutheranism. This specially interested Tony because she saw several instances of a likeness to Cornish customs that savoured of the still older pagan superstitions. In fact Tony became so enamoured of the old Norsk gods that Mary pretended to become alarmed for her soul's health. Mary herself was more interested in the man who was showing them the church. He was a rich old peasant, a kind of local patriarch, highly picturesque in the Telemark costume, differing from that of the ordinary peasant only in being of finer material. His long cloak of vivid green was ornamented on the lapel with a large number of small silver buttons; his hat was of black velvet, very wide-brimmed, with a green band. While Otto was busy translating his bits of information to Tony, Mary was furtively making a small drawing of their guide, with colour notes.

After only a picnic meal at midday on the boat, they were

ready for the hearty supper prepared for them at the farm. But something had gone wrong about Otto's instructions, and much to his annoyance there was not enough sleeping accommodation for the whole party. So the goodwife suggested that perhaps the boys wouldn't mind sleeping on the hay in the barn. Mind! Theo and Joe were only too delighted. To the boys it was a grand excuse for not undressing, and they declared in the morning that they had never slept in such a comfortable bed.

On again the next day, but this time skirting the lake in carrioles. It was Otto's idea of good travelling on a holiday to stop for a look at anything that was alluring, and he ordered a pull-up whenever the girls showed the least inclination. One such stop was to stare at a grand foss, where a river was plunging down a perpendicular depth of some fifty feet. Jammed at the bottom was a huge raft of timber, which they were told had long resisted every effort to dislodge it.

'It's risky business,' said Otto, 'for the moment it does start to move, any man standing on it will be dashed into the rapids and have small chance of his life.'

'Then I hope they'll let it be,' said Tony.

'Not a bit of it,' said Otto, 'some of the men are proud of being nimble and sure-footed, and enjoy trying conclusions with a thing like that. I expect that before long that poor old piece of wood will be doing his duty propping up a part of a Carn Brea mine.'

The next stop was during their passage through a pine forest. Mary noticed a very fragrant odour that she declared must come from *Linnaea borealis*, and they simply must get out to look for it. While the hunt was in progress she told them about Linnaeus and his botanizing triumphs. She had learnt about him, and this flower called after him, at school, and had been on the look-out for it in all her walks round Skien. Sure enough there soon came from her a cry of 'Here it is. I told you so.' She had found an open glade thickly carpeted with the lovely little flowers. Joe insisted on digging up a few roots to take home for the garden of his adored Sophie.

A magnificent midday meal was waiting for them at a farm-house on the lake-side. The main dishes were wild duck and green peas, followed by strawberries and cream— all in such generous quantities that even Theodore and Joe were satisfied. The guest-room was long and low, with great beams in the roof and lattice windows opening on to the lake. The floor was strewn with the young tops of the spruce fir, giving forth a most invigorating odour. Mary couldn't help contrasting the freshness and cleanliness of everything with the conditions of the inns in Spain.

'But everything is a bit too peaceful and kind here,' she added. 'I almost miss the chances of danger that are always waiting round the corner in Spain.'

'Believe me,' said Otto, 'even here we have to cope with a bit of danger now and again.' And as they all went down to the landing-stage to the praam moored ready for them, he added, 'For instance now, this lovely lake has gathered all sorts of folk tales round it. As it has never been fathomed of course it is believed to have no bottom. According to one version this is the mythical goblet that Thor failed to drain. Anyhow it's a poor look-out for any boat that gets upset here. It's perfectly safe of course in fine weather like this.'

The lake was long and narrow, hemmed in by precipitous cliffs coming sheer down to the water's edge with hardly a break or a foothold anywhere. Mary acknowledged that it would be dangerous enough to please the most adventurous to be struggling in this water. Hardly had they gone more than a mile when a sudden squall arose, clouds gathered, stinging rain beat in their faces, and the praam began to rock.

'One of our little Norwegian surprises for you,' said Otto, 'it will soon be over.' But Mary noticed that he had gone rather pale; and he immediately gave some very quick orders to the boatmen. A little way ahead there was a very narrow ledge at the foot of the mountain, where a few trees had managed to take root. It was to this that the boatmen rowed as fast as they could, and pulling in close, they managed to moor the praam to the trunks. There they waited till the storm was over, very wet and aggressively cheerful, to cover the fright they had all had. Tony said it reminded her of the storm in the Gospel, especially when the sun shone gaily out again. The rest of the going was smooth, and evening found them all safely landed at the head of the lake. The night in the farm-house was too much needed by them all to be disturbed by the roar of the river leaving its tumultuous course for the deep lake.

The following morning quite a different method of progress awaited them—one very welcome to the Cornish— horseback. Tethered at the farm-house door waiting for them were some cream-coloured horses. To the alarm of Otto and the guides, Mary, Tony, and Joe were no sooner mounted than off they started at a brisk trot, and with difficulty were persuaded to go more slowly 'lest they should fall off'. Politeness kept them from laughing at this at first, and soon the nature of the rough track was enough to make them moderate their pace.

'How glorious your sister looks on horseback!' said Theo as he caught up with Joe. 'I had no idea a woman could control a horse like that. Did you see how she took that brook just now without any effort at all?'

'Oh, that's nothing,' replied Joe, 'of course I didn't notice it.' But he was secretly pleased at Theo's admiration and proud of Mary's contempt for fear in any form.

'You see,' said Theo, 'we have some dangers on land as well as on the lakes,' and he pointed out blocks of granite here and there in the path that had fallen from a great height. 'When Otto and I asked you to ride more carefully we weren't just foolishly nervous. Very little will start one of these rocks rolling.'

After a few miles of cautious picking their way up the valley, they reached a clearing, and among the birch and pine on the hill-side stood the little church that served the whole district. Otto said they must dismount to look at it more closely, for it was one of the old *stav-kirkers*. He explained that these ancient churches were built entirely of staves, logs of wood cut flat with an axe, before the use of saw and plane. The architecture was on the lines of a pine-tree, designed to resist bad weather of all kinds—drifts of snow and hurricanes of wind. Mary slipped out the little pocket sketch-book she had secreted, and made a rough drawing of the whole from the little pointed bell-turret at the top to the spreading base. Windows were tiny and protected in large numbers of little gables on every side, looking something like cones on a tree.

'What is this kind of cloister all round the base?' she asked Otto.

'While you have been sketching, we have been all round this cloister as you call it, and I've been showing them that it is open only to the outside, and serves as another protection to the church. It gives it stability of course, but it also serves a lot of other purposes. The people use it for meetings, making contracts, and business transactions and whatnot.'

'A kind of centre for the whole population—what a happy plan,' said Tony, 'to have this blessed refuge between that brawling river and the frowning mountains.'

'Yes,' said Otto, 'to this little church all the peasantry for many miles round come for baptism, confirmation, marriage, social life, and business, and finally are brought to be laid to rest in its shadow.'

'Confirmation? do they make much of that?' asked Tony. 'We hear very little of that, if anything at all, in Cornwall.'

'It's quite an important thing here,' said Otto. 'According to Norsk law every boy and girl is confirmed before seventeen. If not, he may be put in prison.'

'In prison!' gasped Tony, 'how very religious Norway must be!'

'Not so religious as it sounds. The clergy have the duty of preparing the young people for the rite, but the work is not confined by any means to religious doctrine. It's done so well that we have the best-educated peasantry in Europe.'

'I suppose they have their lessons in this cloister,' said Tony.

'Yes, and wander round according to the way of the wind, so as to be always to leeward.'

A large farmstead, some ten miles up the valley, was their objective. Here Otto had engaged rooms for them all for a week. This was to be their centre for excursions into the wilder regions round about. Tony was struck with the way in which the farmer's wife received Otto, as though he were some royal personage. She herself was something of a grand lady. Her long, beautifully timbered guest-room contained a rich collection of treasures gathered from her travels during many years. Her chief pride was a service of silver, made from the product of the Kongsberg mine of the province. The girls were more enchanted with the little figures carved in wood, the exquisitely embroidered linen, and the pieces of crockery of unusual design and vivid colour. While they hung over these things, planning which ones they would like to buy for presents to take home, Otto was busy planning too.

'I have brought you,' he said, 'to the very heart of Norway, and we might spend months here, seeing different kinds of scenery all the time. But I have picked out two expeditions, and allowing a day or more at home here between each, for you all to have a rest.'

'I don't want any special expeditions,' said Tony, 'I should be perfectly happy just prowling round these paths that may lead anywhere, and look so inviting.'

But Mary and the boys were all for going as far as they could. Otto said he didn't care what anybody said—they would all have to do his two expeditions. But he added that they mustn't expect too much of them. All next day he was busy finding guides and selecting special horses for the ascent of Gousta, a mountain of over 7,000 feet, standing out prominently alone, commanding views of the whole district.

These horses were cream-coloured like the others, but smaller. 'What they lack in size, they make up in sturdiness and surefootedness,' Otto explained when the guides appeared with them next morning before sunrise at the farmhouse door. The party set off in high spirits up the steep and stony track to the knees of the mountain. After an hour or two of stiff going they reached a considerable plateau, where the girls were astonished to find a human settlement, with herds of cows and flocks of sheep and goats grazing on rich pasture land. Otto gave them a long explanation of the life of the herdsmen up here in the summer months. But what attracted Joe's attention more than this information was Otto's mention of breakfast. They had all started with a mere *café complet,* and a hurried one at that, and he had seen no prospect of anything to eat till they came down again, but he had been too shy to breathe his anxiety on this point even to Theo. His hunger and the oddity of that breakfast impressed it on his memory. How they all laughed! They sat on milking-stools round a tub of sour milk, and each was provided with a wooden spoon. When the milk had been sprinkled with brown sugar, and each had been served with a chunk of rye bread, the simple procedure was to dip the spoon into the tub and convey the milk straight to the mouth.

'Don't let's tell mother about this when we write,' said Mary. 'Let's act it for her when we get home.'

After this a short ride brought them to the foot of the final peak, where they were obliged to dismount, for no horse could carry any one over the rocks to be climbed. The Cornish contingent managed the rocks better than the Norsemen, for they had had plenty of practice on their own seashore. But they were not so much accustomed to snow. Seeing so much of this dazzling stuff so hard and crisp lying in ravines, Joe ran on to it with a shout of joy, but was promptly called off by the guides. In order to give him a wholesome fright, Otto told him that if he fell into one of those ravines nothing could get him out.

'Once,' said he, 'a man fell in when he was up here alone, and was given up for lost. Many years afterwards, in an unusually hot summer when the snow had partially melted, his body was found in a perfect state of preservation, except for the loss of one eye which had been picked by an eagle.' This last touch about the eagle lent a horribly realistic air to the story, and Joe was very quiet for some time, and definitely avoided the ravines.

Another disappointment was awaiting the boy. A sharp rainfall came on, and it was decreed that Joe must go no farther. He was rather delicate, and no risks must be taken. In the midst of his protests Theo came up and offered to go back with him as far as the pasture land, and stay there with him in shelter till the others returned.

Mary and Tony were determined to persevere to the summit, rain or fine, greatly to the admiration of the guides who were obviously amazed at the attempt being made by ladies in any kind of weather. Just as they reached the top they were rewarded by a sudden clearing of the sky, glorious sunshine, and such a view as took the girls' breath away. It was their first experience of seeing a lovely world from a great height, and no previous imagination can ever come near it. Otto had secreted some sandwiches and a flask of wine in his knapsack, and now he brought these out to celebrate the reaching of the top. The guides, too, had secret sources of nourishment. The girls enjoyed the tiny meal in a way that only people who have got to the top of a dangerous mountain can understand. Tony felt it to be a kind of sacrament.

She had been a little anxious about Joe, and sorry for his disappointment. But boylike, he and Theo had made the best of the situation, and had sucked much fun from watching a dairy woman making cheese by a good fire, and at the same time tending a goat that had broken its leg. Boylike, too, they had obtained a meal. 'After all,' said Theo, 'we had a better time than you, for what is a mountain view compared to a broken leg?'

On their return to the farm that night they had to enter their names in the visitors' book, in a list of those who had conquered Gousta. Years afterwards Tony was reading a book about travel in Norway when she came upon this surprising detail: the author mentioned having found an entry in this visitors' book of 'Two English ladies named Vivian, who, to their honour be it spoken, had made the ascent of Gousta.'

The day after the ascent was quite appropriately Sunday, for it was to be a complete rest. Mary kept on blaming Otto for not having told them beforehand of the view they were to expect. But, as he pointed out, if it had continued to rain they wouldn't have had it, and besides it's always better not to talk too much about things before people see them. Tony was dead against going to see anything else, to spoil the effect.

'Well,' said Otto, 'we'll potter about here to-morrow, but if it's fine on Tuesday there's just one little thing I want to show you that's a bit farther off. After that and another day's rest or pottering we will go home.'

Tuesday's weather was all that could be wished, and Otto told them that it would be a new kind of getting about for this expedition—namely entirely on their feet. Fortunately they needed no guides, could start when they liked and take their own time. Otto and Theo each packed a knapsack with provisions for a picnic, prepared for them by the kindly hostess of the farm.

Their route lay along terrace-paths of the mountain sides, among the pines, every turn giving them some entrancing views of hills, streams, and ravines. Sweet scents from the pines and wayside flowers, bright colours from wild berries, the invigorating air—all combined to make the walk a ravishing one.

'I don't believe we are going anywhere,' said Tony, 'it's just the *walk* of a lifetime that Otto has planned for us.'

'Whatever is that noise?' said Mary.

'Only a waterfall,' said Otto, who was leading the little Indian file. 'That's what we have come to see.'

He didn't add then what he told them later on that it was the Rjukan Foss, the mightiest cataract not only in Norway, but in the whole of Europe. The terrific roar was due to the plunging of the Maan River five hundred feet into an abyss that has never been seen because of the continual spray incessantly thrown up. Nature seemed to have made an effort to enhance the scene with every striking effect. In sudden contrast with the tree-clad flowery valley came the appalling force of the torrent, and then, above the clouds of spray, the sunshine was creating an exquisite rainbow.

'Well,' said Mary, 'if you won't let me quote Coleridge here I shall burst—

> *Who bade the Sun*
> *Clothe you with rainbows? Who, with living flowers*
> *Of loveliest blue, spread garlands at your feet?'*

While the girls were indulging their rhapsodies Otto and the boys were spreading out the contents of their knapsacks, supplemented by a good supply of wild strawberries gathered on the way. They chose a spot at a little distance from the roar of the water, but still within sight of the Fall. After the meal no one seemed inclined to move away, so Otto said he would tell them a story about it.

'You see,' said he, 'that narrow ledge in the face of the cliff over there?' It was some time before they could make out this tiny path between the rocky face above and the precipice below, running alongside the Fall.

'A path is it?' said Tony. 'But surely never trodden by man?'

'Oh yes it is. We might even see a peasant going along it to-day, and carrying a bundle too. It is a short cut between two districts which are only connected otherwise by a circuitous route. Now the story goes that a young farmer on one side was in love with a girl living on the other, but he was too poor to marry her. He determined to seek his fortune abroad, and bade her farewell at this their favourite trysting-place, vowing to come back to the same spot at that very same hour, as soon as ever he had made enough money to be married. "If you love me still", said he, "you will be here to meet me." She promised that every day at that hour she would come. It was years before he had made enough money to return, but she never missed a day in coming to the spot. At last one day she saw him coming, waving joyously to her. In their excitement they both rushed forward, missed their footing as they embraced, and fell together down into that seething gulf. Ever since the peasants call it the Marie Pass, after the name of the girl.'

'Romantic,' commented Mary, 'but I think they were silly to meet in such a dangerous place.'

Tony was more serious over it. She thought it was a grand sort of death, and the silliness seemed to her to lie in the wasted years of waiting to be well off, when they might have been happy in poverty. While they were all preparing to start back Otto said to Tony in an undertone 'I'm afraid that story was a bit too tragic for you.' 'No,' she replied, 'not tragic at all—the tragedy would have been if he had fallen and she had had to live on without him— perhaps continuing to come every day to the spot, on the wild chance that he hadn't really come, hadn't really fallen.'

After supper that evening there was one point in which they were all agreed—that Otto had kept the best till last, and they found it difficult to thank him. But it was obvious that their enthusiasm was gratitude enough. And now Mary and Tony approached the mistress of the farm on the delicate matter of buying the pieces of crockery, embroidery, and carving that they had ear-marked as presents to take back to the Barnholts and their people at home.

'Now which pieces did you fancy?' she inquired. When they pointed out their desires, she exclaimed 'Certainly, my dears, take them, you are more than welcome to them.' She was so shocked at the idea of taking money for such trifles that they could say no more. Of course they found that they had no room for more than three very little and unpretentious bits of wood-carving.

§ 5

They took the return journey at a quicker pace, for all were anxious to get back to Skien and relate their adventures to the Barnholts. No more going away, no more sight-seeing for us, we have seen the best possible—that was the determined policy of Mary and Tony. But the Barnholts maintained that it would never do to go back to England without visiting the capital, where there was so much to see and do, people to meet and shops to sample.

As a journey it turned out to be a tame affair after their mountain experiences, for they went by steam-boat from Brevig to Christiania. The best hotel was their head-quarters, but they spent little time in it, for the city seemed to be mainly populated with friends and relations of the Barnholts, pressing invitations on them. It was owing to the Barnholts' influence in high quarters that they had per-mission to see every part of the royal palace. This had been begun twenty years before and was now nearing comple-tion. Originally it was quite in the country, but was being gradually connected with the city by a grand new street, with fine buildings on each side, making a dignified approach to the palace.

Mary was in her element in all the social gatherings and in squandering her money buying presents in the shops, but she was almost as glad as Tony to return to the homelike Skien and the daily pottering about the fjord and the evenings round the fireside.

Autumn was soon upon them, and letters from Reskadinnick were agitating for their return. One from their father gave instructions for their coming home by way of Germany, so as to see a little more while they were about it. 'So like father,' said Mary, 'always for seeing what's round the corner.' Otto threw himself with energy into the plan for their journey, so as to make it almost from door to door entirely unlike the route by which they had come. They all knew that he was in the depths of low spirits at their going (for he was not good at hiding his feelings), and therefore they encouraged his activity over the plans.

'Instead of going down the fjord as you came first,' said he, 'you shall drive to Brevig.'

It was a November morning when the wrench was at hand. The carriage stood at the door, with the luggage packed on it. Mr. and Mrs. Barnholt, Yetta and Sophie, Theodore, and the whole staff of servants in the background stood around while the Cornish visitors took their seats. But where was Otto? No one had seen him for the last hour or so. Mary felt anxious, for she could see that Tony was having a great struggle to appear polite and pour forth expressions of gratitude.

Suddenly Otto came rushing out of the house like a whirlwind, flung a bag to the coachman, and jumped into the carriage. 'It was no use,' he cried, 'I simply could not let you go away without me,' with a special glance at Tony. He had been making hurried arrangements about his work so that he might go with them as far as Germany. 'It wouldn't be safe,' he added, laughing, 'for you to be going to strange countries by yourselves.' Mary's heart warmed to him in gratitude, and she no longer bothered to see how Tony was feeling.

Meanwhile little Joe was all eyes for his new surroundings, and as they were boarding a steam-boat at Brevig he noticed two little naval cadets bound like themselves for Gothenburg. He managed to get into conversation with them on the way, and of course they were only too pleased to inflame his longing for the Navy by telling him of all the glories that they themselves were expecting. He, too, had something to tell, in his experience of fjord navigation and his story of Paul Jones. This chance encounter stood out beyond all the other charms of the holiday, for it filled out in glowing colours Joe's dream of what his life was to be.

The bare scenery of Sweden seemed tame to them after the wooded hills of Norway, and their two days' stay in Gothenburg, spent in a conscientious visiting of everything of importance, left no impression but that of 'a fine city'.

Copenhagen, their next port of call, was another contrast, full of interest to each of them. The grand harbour set Joe questioning Mary about Nelson's victory there. She was full of description and anecdote about his eye, but when he asked her why Nelson was attacking the Danes she was stumped. 'I fancy,' she said, 'that the Danes had rather too good a fleet to please Nelson, and he thought he had better damp them down a bit.' 'What fun!' said Joe, 'I'd love a fight like that.'

The main interest for the girls was the work of Thorwaldsen. His death a year or two before had been a great grief to the Danes, and he was the chief topic of conversation. All visitors were expected to admire his colossal statues of Christ and the twelve apostles. Mary and Tony were not agreed about them, Mary being deeply impressed with the workmanship in the detail, and Tony thinking them rather flat and uninspired in feeling. Otto went rather farther in his dislike of them: 'Too holy altogether' was his verdict. 'They were most of them fishermen, weren't they?'

A surprise awaited them on their return to their hotel the second evening of their stay in Copenhagen: there stood brother William at the entrance. He had been sent by his father to escort them home. Otto was very cordial in his greeting, but could find no excuse for not going back to Norway. William begged him to come back to Cornwall with them, but he said that he had only snatched this leave and ought not to make it any longer. However, a parting can express a great deal, and Tony looked happy enough as they embarked for Kiel.

The Danish countryside from Kiel to Altona was more like England than anything they had seen for many months, and they enjoyed the drive among the farm-houses built of clay and roofed with thatch. Two days in Hamburg were as much as they wanted, and their chief memory of the place was their visit to the theatre. William obtained tickets for some good seats, without understanding the name of the play, or indeed caring. They were a little late in going in, and soon discovered that the play was a capital farce. Mary was proud of her grasp of the foreign dialogue, and explained the theme in whispers to William and Tony, and the situations were so funny that all three were soon in fits of laughter. The people near them, however, did not seem to be amused at all—rather annoyed, so Tony thought. Presently an attendant bore down on William and poured forth a stream of German at him, gesticulating and pointing to the exit. At last it dawned on William that they were listening to a tragedy, and he hastily summoned the girls to come out before they disgraced themselves any further.

Their ignorance of German was more troublesome when they were leaving. Luggage and passengers were all packed on the cab when the driver came to the window to ask where they were going. His pointing was sufficient to indicate his question. While William and Tony were looking hopefully at Mary, who was trying French in vain and shaking her head, Joe came to the rescue. He suddenly remembered the word that Otto had used for the steam-boat in Brevig, and shouted 'damp skib'. The driver laughed, nodded, and drove straight to the docks. The name of the vessel, *The Princess Royal* did the rest. It was obvious from the name that she was newly built, and Joe was enchanted with all her appointments, the polished wood everywhere and the spacious saloon with doors opening on to the main deck. In spite of a rough and wintry passage they were none of them ill, and on the second morning they were in sight of the English coast. Here they were hailed by a Yarmouth fishing-boat, and provided with an appetizing breakfast of fresh herrings.

That same evening they landed, spent the night in a London hotel, and were able to go all the way to Exeter by train. One night at Exeter, and then the mail-coach for Cornwall. Only one inside seat was to be had, and this was assigned to Joe. The others had to brave the wettest journey of their lives. It rained in torrents all the way to Okehampton and across Bodmin Moor to Truro. Water streamed from their hats whenever they moved their heads a bit, and was even seeping through to their skin. If it hadn't been for Mary, who saw fresh cause for laughter in each new misery, they would all have had bad chills. As it was they were none the worse, and luxuriated in the roaring fire that welcomed them in the Royal Hotel at Truro. There was time for change of clothes and a hot meal before the coach for Camborne was at the door. The weather had cleared, and by nightfall they had reached Tyack's Hotel in Camborne, and were in the loving embraces of their father and mother, who had the carriage ready to take them to Reskadinnick.

FOUR

JOHN

§ 1

CORNWALL was a different place to the two girls on their return from Norway.

For Tony, all her former duties took on a new lustre. Housekeeping had a fresh zest, as a preparation for the future. In cooking she experimented with the ways they had in Norway. She had picked up hints on preserving fruits, on producing bigger and better eggs, and on the rearing of ducks. She intended to start keeping turkeys. She now knew more about the treatment of the bees, and she had some things to tell the gardener about pruning the fruit trees.

The younger children had always been dear to her, but now she saw still more in them, and as she had them round her, supposed to be 'helping' and for ever asking questions, her dreams ran forward, and she pictured the children that might come to Otto and herself. It was with the children that she indulged her literary imagination. Round the legends of Thor and Woden she made up endless stories to meet the incessant demand. Her descriptions of the winding fjords, the dark forests, the unfathomed lakes, the roaring cataracts—all lent reality to the tales. Sometimes a story involved dark rites in which the devil appeared. He drew a chalk circle, and no one dared cross it. One story told of how the devil turned a man's head right round, so that he had to walk backwards. Often Tony would increase the mystery by stopping short, shaking her head, and saying that 'nobody knew any more about that', or 'no one ever saw him again', or 'it wouldn't do to tell you what happened next'.

She taught them to repeat verses in Norsk, and played Norwegian dance tunes for them to make rhythmic movements as they sang them. Her touch on the piano had now become so light and bewitching that no one could keep still when she swung out one of those dances. Often she would look round to see both Mary and her mother dancing with the children.

To Mary Reskadinnick had become dearer than ever. As she had contrasted its security with the hazards of Spain, she now contrasted its soft warm air and the homeliness of the surrounding lanes with the grand austerity of Norway. The sheltered fjords were all very well, but for her there was nothing to equal the rugged Cornish coast, and a canter along the green turf on the cliffs, with the bite of a sou'-wester on her cheek, to persuade her feelingly of harder things.

No one was ever idle at Reskadinnick, and Mary's duties were clear. Every morning Joe, Lizzie, Emily, and now little Fan as well, were seated round the breakfast-parlour table, and set to their various tasks of reading, writing, grammar, history, geography, French, and even a little adding. Joe had developed so much with his holiday that she began him in Latin and some simple astronomy. He became as fond of this as was Mary herself, for he felt it would help in his seamanship. He liked to find the Pole-star that Mary told him used to be called the Punic star, because the Phoenicians found their way by it. 'That's the star that brought them here to Cornwall,' he would say to himself.

Both Mary and Tony encouraged the children to use their pencils for drawing, and they were even allowed to dabble with Mary's big paint-box. One day baby Fan pointed to the saffron-cake and said 'Weller'. 'What did you say, darling?' asked Mary. 'Weller—weller—weller,' insisted Fan. At last in despair she said, 'Well den, it's pink.'

What Mary enjoyed best was teaching them to ride—to mount their ponies properly, hold the reins correctly, give the right touch for a canter or a gallop, take easy jumps, and not to make a fuss if they were thrown.

A very elastic *ménage* made it difficult to separate duty from pleasure at Reskadinnick. Anybody would drop anything to join in a new happening, to welcome a visitor, to run to see what the postman had brought, to search for lost keys, to bewail the burning of a pan of milk, to find a hen who had laid astray, or to suggest a picnic because the weather was so fine. It was only when a pig was killed that every one had to stand by to help. There was room for no other duty or pleasure. The pig was like some great personage lying in state. His presence, radiating from the kitchen table, seemed to pervade every corner and require the services of young and old, until the joints for more immediate use were stowed in the dairy, those for remoter consumption were put through strange rubbings and placed in the great stone bath, and all the odd pieces were made into sausages for supper and breakfast.

Mary and Tony managed to scrape some time for their

hobbies of sketching and reading. The sea and rocks gave plenty of subjects, but trees were too difficult, and the great elms by the lawn seemed to laugh at their efforts. Tony sighed for the pines of Norway, with their regular outlines against the sky.

'Give me the trees that can't be done,' said Mary, 'rather than your accommodating pines—all alike.'

A fine edition of Shakespeare in several volumes was in continual demand. *Twelfth Night* specially took Tony's fancy; she could never say why, except that it was dreamy, and she loved Feste, with his final song. *Much Ado* fitted Mary's liveliness, and Beatrice was her idea of what a girl should be, with her mischievous wit and impulsiveness. It was this last trait that induced her frequent exclamation, 'Oh that I had been writ down an ass!' much to the puzzlement of her acquaintances. Miss Austen's tales were an endless pleasure. There was an exact Miss Bates living in Camborne, and some one perilously like Mrs. Elton. Here too was a fatal attraction for Mary. 'I feel for Emma; she is always indulging her wit at the expense of other people and then wishing she hadn't. I believe she must have gone on in the same way after she was married, or life would have been dull for Knightly.'

The visitors who were continually dropping in at all hours were for the most part young men, connected with Cap'n Vivian in his mining or farming or other activities, or else the sons of county people living within a morning's ride. Summer weather was the jolliest, perhaps, but there were compensating events when autumn came on. In the hunting-field Mary was at her best, a perfect horsewoman.

One day she happened to be riding a little way ahead of William and Tony, and passed some people in a lane. They stood staring at her, and stopped William as he came up, with 'Excuse me, but who is that lady riding ahead?'

'That,' said William in a serious undertone, 'is the Princess Estremadura, travelling incognito.'

Since she didn't know what fear was, she was able to impart her confidence to her horse and make him do whatever she wanted. To catch her eye and win her admiration was the ambition of most of the young huntsmen. A conceited young fellow named Budge was boasting at the meet one morning of the prowess of his horse, greatly impressing Miss Vivian apparently.

'Can he really!' she exclaimed, 'how splendid!'

He rode off by her side, and seized the chance to propose marriage to this understanding girl who knew a good horse when she saw it. Apparently not quite catching what he said she replied, 'Just a moment. Wait till we are over this hedge coming.'

'Certainly, but it's too high to jump. I'll ride along and look for a gate or a gap.'

'Oh, no,' said Mary, 'allow me to give you a lead,' and with a touch to her horse she went over clean, and was well away out of sight by the time he had managed to get round, for his horse had refused even the lead.

Tony and Mary had many a hearty laugh in private over the various ways in which she evaded the continual offers of marriage. On this occasion the talk ran, 'Who was it to-day, Mary?'

'Young Budge, but I headed him off easily, so that

he could imagine he hadn't said anything. I just rode away.'

'But didn't he try again?'

'No, I had put him off his stride—altogether, I hope.'

A dance was a more prolific source for love affairs than the hunting-field. In addition to the informal dances that were started at any time, there were plenty of more elaborate ones in the country houses or in more distant towns. An invitation arrived one day for a dance at Scorrier. With the two girls the first question was of course 'What shall we wear?' followed by the inevitable conclusion 'We haven't a rag to put on.'

'Camborne shops are so uninspired,' said Mary. 'We must go into Truro, and see what it can do.'

The question of expense did not trouble them. Tony and all the younger ones were given pocket-money on a sliding scale according to age, and Tony had always managed to save up a bit. Mary was on a different footing; she was allowed to go to any shop and order what she fancied, and had come to think it undignified to ask the price of anything. Her father paid the bill willingly, for she had no desire for extravagance and showed excellent taste in all she bought.

An early start brought them to Truro in good time for a first look round in the morning. Leaving their horses at the Royal Hotel, they made for the leading draper's. Sherry and cake were at once brought, and after a social chat the main business was broached, and the latest designs from London were produced and discussed. Then materials suitable and unsuitable were flashed forth, 'just for Miss Vivian to see'.

She was struck with one in a new shade of mauve. 'Ah, that has lately arrived from Paris, madam; it is no wonder you admire it.' Tony chose a dark purple, to be a kind of contrast. Then all the staff of the shop were ordered to go ahead with the measuring and cutting out, and by the time the girls had returned from their midday meal at the hotel the essential fittings were ready to try on.

After business, pleasure, and Tony, who had brought plenty of ready money, insisted on buying presents to take home to the others—a handkerchief for mother, a book of tales for Lizzie, a little hunting-crop for Emily, a doll for Fan, and greatest treasure of all, a big toy boat for Joe.

Then Mary drew the line at festooning the horses with any more parcels, and they rode home in the gathering dusk to find the children eagerly awaiting their return, and even Fan allowed to sit up. The new doll was a great help in getting her off to bed, for it could be cuddled down by her side; but Joe's boat couldn't be sailed till the next day.

The dresses arrived in good time, were tried on and criticized at a family parade some time before the actual day; Cap'n Vivian noted the colours and bought a new fan for each girl to match her dress. The dance was announced to begin at nine, and Sammy was told to bring the carriage round at eight. Early in the evening he came to the kitchen door asking to speak to Miss Mary. Be ready a bit earlier could she? The roads were that slippery he would have to go dead slow.

'No, Sammy, don't be a minute earlier than eight. I want to be late; make it quarter past, and if we're delayed on the way quite a lot, so much the better.'

'Very good, Miss.' He knew that what Miss Mary wanted was the only thing to bother about.

She was a long time over her dressing, and Tony came to her room to see how she was getting on. Mary was usually so quick that Tony was surprised to see her fussing over some trifling alteration.

'It's splendid, Mary. I never saw you look so well. Don't alter it. What necklace will you wear with that mauve?'

'None at all, nothing will go with it, and besides I want to wear as little ornament as possible.'

'Well then do hurry along. William is down in the hall, getting fearfully impatient, scolding Sammy for being late, and grumbling at you for keeping the horses standing. It's more than half-past eight now, and it's a long drive.'

At last they started, but they were only a little way down the drive when Mary suddenly exclaimed that she had left her fan behind. No, she couldn't possibly do without it, and William had to get out and go back for it, after very full instructions as to where it probably had been left. When they were once past the gravelled drive the going had to be slower, for every now and again one of the horses would slip on the slightly frozen road. Soon Sammy turned into a lane that would take them round a rather longer way. Out went William's head: why was he going right out of the direction? didn't he know the way to Scorrier? Sammy explained that the lane was more sheltered and the going not so slippery. But even so he drove absurdly cautiously, and William kept looking at his watch and fuming at the delay. About a quarter of a mile from the house in Scorrier one of the horses stumbled badly. Sammy pulled up and came round to the door. Could the young ladies manage to walk the rest of the way? He would be able to get everything right for the return journey, but just now he couldn't.

'That's all right,' cried Mary. 'If you will carry our shoes, William, and lead the way, Tony and I can carry our fans and gather up our skirts. It's lucky the moon is up.'

'You seem very cheerful about it,' said Tony as they began their walk, 'but how horribly late we shall be.'

'That's the very thing I want. Can't you see that I've been wasting time on purpose?'

'But whatever for?'

'It's all very well to be in fairly good time for our dances in Camborne, but with people like these Lanyons who think themselves a bit superior and pronounce their name in an absurd way, it doesn't do to appear anxious to come. Far better to arrive fresh, just for a "look-in" when every one else is a bit jaded.'

'What fun! I should never have thought of that.'

'Nor should I. It was one of the hints they gave us at Bath; be the last to come and the first to go.'

As Mary predicted, their entrance made something of a stir in the party. The walk in the frosty weather gave a glow to their cheeks, and their arrival was like a breath of fresh air. A dance was just over, and the young men were soon gathering around them asking for engagements for those still to come. 'We were afraid you weren't coming' was the constant remark. Tony noticed that Mary made no reference to wayside troubles, but merely said 'Oh yes, we started late'.

After supper came the main event of the evening, the cotillion. This was a square dance involving some rather difficult figures, with graceful curtsies and bows and passing under uplifted arms. Mary had learnt it at Bath, and was able to lead it so that it went without any hitch. It was customary during the last figure for each lady dancer to be presented with a piece of jewellery, as valuable as the hostess cared to make it, and custom also demanded that the recipient should put it on at once. The gift that fell to Mary that night was a necklet of uncut amethysts. The effect on her mauve dress was like a touch of magic. Almost immediately afterwards Mary decided that they must go home, and to Tony's bitter disappointment she left the necklet on the dressing-table.

'You see, Tony, I didn't get that best gift of all by honest chance; it was engineered my way by Robert Lanyon. He was just a shade too friendly. He will understand why it was left behind. No, it will not be sent on to me.'

However late their return, Mary and Tony always had a talk before bed on the events of the evening. A short but never to be forgotten talk followed one festive evening at Reskadinnick:

'Young Budge left very early to-night, didn't he, Mary?'

'Yes; the fact is that he was not fit to stay on, either physically or mentally.'

'Sounds mysterious. Too much of father's old port? I saw him going at it.'

'Doubtless. But also' (here Mary broke off to laugh) 'he had too much of me.'

'Good, I hope you snubbed him—I can't bear the fellow.'

'Oh dear no; I wouldn't pay him the compliment. But after the one dance that I was obliged to give him he suggested a stroll in the moonlight round the front lawn. It was certainly better than dancing with him. He was definitely "not himself", to put it mildly, and tried to kiss me. As I gave a sudden jerk aside to avoid it this long pin in my hair did its duty nobly—gave him a scratch right across his face —a downright nasty one—a sobering one, Tony.'

'Well, I hope you said you were sorry.'

'Sorry! I was never so overjoyed. I burst out laughing, and told him it served him right for trying to steal what no decent girl would ever give him.'

'That would make him pretty mad.'

'It did. He dashed off, and I suppose went home at once. A pleasant memory, Tony. An act of God.'

'Quite, but I have misgivings. He is the sort of man to have it back on you if he can.'

Far more enjoyable in many cases than the dance itself was the day following. All the young men made it their duty to ride round to call on their hostess, ostensibly to inquire how she was after the fatigues of the preceding day, and in reality to have further chats and so on with the girls. The informality was the main charm, and for this Reska-dinnick was endowed by nature and—not art, but artless-ness. Mrs. Vivian never had any fatigue to talk about, and managed to concoct plenty of interesting refreshments, not left-overs from the day before ('funeral baked-meats' as Mary called them). The young men arrived singly or in couples, tethered their horses anywhere, and discovered the girls at their work, which was immediately dropped for strolls about the grounds, while the children romped about, eating the cakes and begging for rides on the strange horses.

Tony was in great demand on these occasions. Although she never spoke of Otto, there was a general vague knowledge that she was probably going to marry some one she had met in Norway. So it was safe to be quite friendly with her, and as her own happiness was infectious she was a capital companion. She was specially sympathetic over love-affairs, always ready to listen to descriptions of enchantment or to miserable tales of rejection. Her advice—that was what was in demand in the latter case. Unfortunately these sad cases were often concerned with Mary. What could be done to win her? On this point Tony was as blank as the rejected ones.

Of Mary herself the neighbourhood was a little afraid. She had the character of being learned. Not that she ever talked of learned matters. Quite the contrary; it was mainly because she openly despised learning and knowledge of facts that the fear rose. There was the vague feeling that it is only those who know a good deal who can afford to despise learning, and they never knew where they were with her. Sometimes she would slip out a long word by mistake, as on some occasion of a tea-party she exclaimed 'What a heterogeneous mass of cakes!' To the hostess the expression savoured of something unpleasant, and word went round Camborne that Miss Vivian had been making rude reflections on the food that was put before her.

Her eyes, too, looked mischievous, as if she were enjoying some secret joke. And at whose expense? She came to be called the Sphinx. But when her face broke into a sudden smile a man would lose his head and as often as not propose marriage out of hand.

'You simply must not smile on a young man,' said Tony to her, after one of the many confidences.

'But I've tried being dead serious and stand-offish, and that seems to make things worse. They think of me as a *femme incomprise*—an attraction in itself. By the way, I didn't notice young Budge here this morning. Did he turn up?'

'No, he didn't come.'

'Perhaps,' laughed Mary, 'his scratch is still showing. Or he may be still offended.'

'Both, I'm afraid. Young Bolitho, who sees a good deal of him, told me all about it, and said that he was still nursing his wrath when he called for him this morning.'

'What fun!' said Mary, 'quite an Achilles.'

'Not so funny, because he had made out that you had done it on purpose, and he meant to have his revenge.'

'What villainy has he in mind, Tony? Will he set Reska-dinnick on fire, or knife father, or send me sweets with crushed glass in them?'

'Do be serious. He may spread ugly tales about you. One is never safe from a liar.'

'Well then, if one is never safe it's no use to bother.'

§ 2

One summer morning news went round the house that the postman had brought an interesting letter. Such a rumour was always the signal for every one to gravitate to the front kitchen. This was in no sense a kitchen, but the name remained because it had been the kitchen of the original old farm-house. With one door leading into the real kitchen, another leading into the breakfast-parlour, and another into the garden, it became the focus of the whole house, and was used for all family consultations and exchange of news. The children were the first to drop their sums in the breakfast-parlour and clamber into the window-seat, wide-eyed, expectant. Tony was in the middle of kneading a batch of saffron cake, and came in from the kitchen all floury-handed. Joe, who was at home on holiday from school, had seen the postman in the drive, had had a peep at the letters and scented a strange one, and had followed him up. Their father, mother, and Mary were busy with the letter. It was from John Symons, saying that he had arrived in Falmouth, just returned from his long station in the West Indies, and proposing to spend a few days of his leave with Mrs. Vivian and her family, in accordance with the kind invitation he had received some time back in Falmouth, hoping that it would cause no inconvenience, and also hoping that he would have the pleasure of renewing his acquaintance with her daughter.

The children vaguely connected the name John Symons with Mary's journey to Spain. As soon, therefore, as they gathered that the letter was from him, they went all Spanish, and began blowing kisses in all directions in what Mary had told them was the Spanish manner: bunching their fingers together at the mouth and then opening them out with a sweeping gesture towards the person to be saluted. As soon as they took in the fact that John was actually coming to visit them they showed their approval by jumping up on the great white wooden table and executing the fandango that Mary had taught them.

Meanwhile the elders were discussing the best ways of making John as welcome as possible. The first thing to do was to write a letter in reply. This, of course, had to come from Mrs. Vivian, but Cap'n Vivian was to write also, to arrange a day and hour for meeting him at Tyack's Hotel, where the coach stopped. Joe was perhaps the most excited of all, for he had no end of important points about life in the Navy that would now have a chance of being settled. The main task for his mother was to prepare a bedroom, and Tony began a rapid survey of the food supply and the means of supplementing it. As for Mary, her immediate job was to answer the incessant questions of Joe and the little girls: What's he like? Can he ride? Will he play with us? What is the name of his vessel? How many masts has she got? What will he be dressed like? Will he be black after being in the West Indies?

Mary took care to give very dull answers. She described him as rather plain, not very tall, a bit bronzed, but nothing so exciting as black, severe-looking, silent, he could certainly dance, but she doubted whether he could ride well or even swim—she had heard that naval men frequently couldn't.

As Mary had hoped, all these forebodings of dullness and severity heightened the effect when he arrived and turned out to be extremely good-looking, full of high spirits, with charming manners to every one. The children practically claimed him as their property, and to amuse them he had as many stories of hairbreadth escapes as Othello.

'Have you ever been in a sea-fight?' asked Joe.

'Sorry to say I have not,' he replied, 'but I know a story about one, and one too where the chief hero was a boy just about your age, Joe. His name was Hopson, and he ran away to sea. Now there was war on at the time and he was hurried into a ship just starting off. In a few hours after he had joined her she was in the middle of a fierce engagement with the French fleet. After doing blindly what he was told for a long time, he asked when the battle would be over. "We shall go on," said the sailor by his side, "until that flag up there at the enemy's masthead is pulled down!" Well, if that's all the row is about, thought young Hopson, I'll see what I can do. The masts of the French and British ships were lying side by side in the smoke, like this'—here John made a rapid sketch to show the position. 'So Hopson ran up the rigging quite quietly and managed to seize the French flag without being noticed. Before he could smuggle it down to his own deck there were cries of victory from the British. The French, thinking that their flag had been struck, left their guns, and the British boarded their vessel and took them. Of course, Hopson was proud of what he had done, and boasted to the sailors around him. They were puzzled what to do about it and reported him to the Admiral, wondering what on earth would be done to him. The Admiral burst out laughing, and told young Hopson that if he went on getting such fine results he would be an admiral himself one day. And so he was.'

Joe squared his shoulders with pleasure and hoped to match John's story with one of his father's that they all knew well. 'Father was in a real war once, weren't you, father?' said he.

'Well, not exactly, my boy, but I was certainly once mixed up in a kind of engagement when the great war was on. You see, John, I happened to be in one of the Falmouth packets going to Lisbon, just at the time when Sir Arthur Wellesley went to take command of the army sent out to check Soult. The crew of the packet were called upon to be exercised in the use of the boarding-pike. Of course, I joined in with them, though I was totally ignorant of the use of the pike. As soon as the pikes had been served out to us all, the order rang out "Repel boarders on the starboard bow". Away we all scampered to meet the imaginary foe supposed to be forcing a way on board. Running a bit too eagerly I drove my pike at the man in front of me and sent him sprawling on the deck—not really injured but pretty wild. Just like young Hopson I was ordered aft to hear the worst. When my stupidity was reported to the Captain he too laughed heartily, but felt it his duty to let forth a stream of abuse at me, bits of which I still remember but needn't repeat.'

'You were lucky, sir, to take even that part in the war. It looks as if there were going to be no such chance for you and me, doesn't it, Joe? Endless peace—that's what it looks like. I suppose you never had any actual engagement off this awful coast of ours, did you, sir?'

'No, hardly that. But we once had a prize. You have been to Portreath, haven't you?'

'Yes, it was only the other day that your daughters and I were riding by there.'

'Well, you noticed the tiny harbour. That little affair was constructed and fitted with a battery away back in the early days of George III, when we were fighting the French in all parts of the world. They were very proud of their defences, though what sane vessel would ever make an attack on our Cornish coast I can't imagine. The people of Portreath have stories enough of relics of ships that have been dashed against the rocks and swallowed up by the sea. Bits of planks, a few oranges, or a keg of foreign butter—that was the kind of trace. Once a Newfoundland dog survived, and once a black man reached the shore alive, but died almost immediately. Of course, any vessel caught on this coast in one of our special sou'-westers will try to make any port she can. Well, one day during the exciting times when the Cornish folk were expecting Bony to land at any moment (poor fellow, I should have been sorry for him if he had tried!) a French vessel was in difficulties and sailed safely into Portreath. The long-expected moment had come, and every blessed man, woman, and child crowded up to look. The battery was, with great difficulty, I believe, made to say something, and as the Frenchman had only a couple of guns she thought it best to get away. Then happened one of the joys of Cornwall—she couldn't get out!'

'What a prize!' exclaimed John. 'I can see those people of Portreath having the time of their lives, can't you, Joe?'

John's treatment of Joe as a future naval man drew forth the boy's complete devotion. But each member of the family was attracted to him for one reason or another. Mrs. Vivian felt warmly towards him because he was an only child and had lost his mother, and appeared to have no near relations except his father, whom she suspected of being rather severe. She begged him to make his stay as long as possible, so as to enjoy the many invitations that poured in when the neighbourhood knew of his arrival. These were pleasing, no doubt, but he insisted that he liked best to potter about Reskadinnick.

He appeared to seek the company of Tony more than any one else, and it didn't escape her notice that he would use every device to get her to talk about Mary. 'Does your sister like so and so?' 'Where was your sister at that time?' and so on. On the other hand, Tony noticed that Mary never mentioned him, even in the girls' confidential chats. This was a good sign, for Tony knew that when Mary felt most she said least. So everything promised well for the long-cherished hope of a love-match. Mary's words could be repressed but not her happiness, and Tony thought she had never seen her sister look so lovely, nor seem to be in such genuine high spirits.

Although John betrayed his feelings quite obviously in his chats with Tony, he never referred to Mary by name. After a few days he ventured to bring out his private manuscript book to show Tony. This consisted of tinted pages of superfine paper, bound in a richly decorated leather cover —all ready for contributions. On each of the first dozen or so pages was a poem, with here and there the drawing of a ship in delicate pencil strokes. Each poem or drawing was carefully dated and located 'at sea' at such and such a latitude and longitude. H.M.B. *Ranger* must have been a steady vessel, or the sea very calm, or John had extraordinary control of his muscles, for the penmanship was exquisite. The drawings, however, were done in harbour, and bore the names of the places touched—Trinidad, Barbados, Hayti, and so on.

When Tony saw the drawings she said, 'Wait a moment, I must fetch Mary to see these.'

'Why, you can *draw*!' cried Mary. 'Let's go for a sketching expedition—to the cliffs will be best.'

Her eye then rested on some of the poems, and one caught her attention; it was couched in terms of deepest devotion, and whenever the name of the person addressed would naturally occur there was a blank. She bent over it, was aware that John was watching intently, and felt obliged to make some remark more appropriate than mere admiration of the handwriting. Finding no literary merit whatever, she could think of nothing better to say than: 'What is the name of the girl that you have left out in this one?' Seeing John's self-conscious face she added hurriedly: 'Sorry. I didn't mean to be inquisitive. Come along, Tony, let's all go out now and try a bit of sketching in the garden.'

It was obvious to Tony that the omitted name in the poem was 'Mary'. She had noticed that while John called them all by their Christian names—Tony, Lizzie, Emily, Fan— he never addressed Mary by name at all. Of course, Mary had noticed this too, and the poems showed her how John had been thinking of her continually ever since their meeting in Falmouth, and it was obvious in a hundred ways that he could think of little else now.

'What a mercy,' said her mother to Cap'n Vivian, 'that Mary seems to have found some one at last that she really cares for. I was beginning to fear that she never would— so fastidious as she always is.'

'She will never come across a finer fellow than John. She is proud of him, I can see. They seem just made for one another.'

Those were gloriously happy days for all at Reskadinnick, for elders, children, and all, for John and Mary were not too much absorbed in one another, and lovely summer weather smiled on most of their long rides and picnics and sketching expeditions with the younger ones.

But Tony was not absolutely satisfied. Mary's happiness was almost as much a concern to her as her own, and she watched her sister closely. Their confidential chats at the end of the day had practically ceased, so that she had nothing but her observation to judge by. What struck her uncomfortably after a while was the persistence with which Mary was continually summoning her to join them when she and John were booked for a walk or a ride. There were urgent whispers in Mary's not-to-be-denied tones: 'You come too, Tony.' Funny. She and Otto had never been able to get enough time alone together for the heaps they had to say, and for their heavenly bits of love-making. What was the matter? John was eager enough for any chance to have Mary to himself. Although full of politeness when Tony reluctantly mounted her horse and trotted after them, he could not disguise his disappointment by his over-hearty expressions.

Catching Mary alone one morning in the front-kitchen Tony ventured: 'Anything wrong between you and John?'

'Oh no. Only that I've been playing Beatrice to one who is no Benedick,' was the ominous reply as Mary slid away into the garden.

The day of John's departure to join his ship was close at hand. He was to leave very early on a Thursday morning. On the Tuesday night Mary came into Tony's room in her old accustomed way. But this time she sat down and burst into tears. Such a thing had never happened before. Mary in tears! Tony knew that it must be something serious, so she went on brushing her hair without a word, without even turning her head. When Mary seemed a little calmer, 'So distressed at John's having to go?' This was only a feeler, an opening to help Mary, for Tony knew it was something far else.

An indignant toss of the head, with a muttered, 'What do you take me for?' was the only reply.

'Not come to the point, has he?'

'Come to the point! Why, he does little else.'

'Well, what's the trouble then? Surely you love him? He's a man in ten thousand.'

'Yes, yes, he is—all that heart can desire.'

'Well then?'

'Oh, Tony, he loves me too much.'

'Too much! What absurdity! That's impossible. You know how mother always says that we need never fear loving any one too much, so long as we love *enough*.'

'Yes, exactly. Well, then, he doesn't love me enough. Oh, Tony darling, he worships me. No woman can stand being worshipped. Ask yourself—How would you like it if Otto worshipped you?'

Tony laughed at the very idea. 'That would be ridiculous. Otto knows my follies and shortcomings, and I expect he's got plenty, too. Anyhow, they wouldn't make any difference. Now you talk about it, I must say it would be dreadful to be regarded as perfect. Otto and I have got inside one another's minds, and we can laugh at failings and such outside things.'

'Laugh,' interrupted Mary. 'Now you've struck it. Otto can laugh and John can't.'

'Whatever do you mean? John's laugh—why, it's as ready and hearty as any I've heard. He's far more full of gaiety than Otto.'

'Tony, you don't understand. Laughter and gaiety in themselves are nothing. It's the underlying sense of humour that matters. One can have that without ever laughing at all. Otto has it, and John hasn't—there you are.'

'But what makes you think so?'

'Listen, Tony. When we are alone together John is a different man. He gets all agitated—into a kind of tremble.'

'That's just because he is so anxious about winning your love. You wouldn't like him to be too confident?'

'Yes, I should—anything sensible. He has breathed his love no end of times, but never once attempted to kiss me.'

'Good gracious! Never mind, Mary, he'll get over all that when you are married.'

'Very likely he would, or I should die of boredom. But then, too, all my faults would be the more glaring. And you know how one comes to dislike anybody that one has worshipped.'

'Yes, like the Teagues. You remember how he used to adore his wife—and now look at them.'

'Well, what am I to do about it? To-morrow is his last

day, and I am dreading beyond words our inevitable final good-bye. I think I must tell the plain truth.'

'No, Mary, I wouldn't if I were you. I've found it wiser never to give people reasons, especially true ones. They simply override them one after the other. You say you haven't the money and can't afford it, and they reduce the price or say you can pay later on. You say you can't come because you have work to do—the work can wait. You don't feel well—it'll do you good to come out.'

Mary laughed and agreed. 'What *do* you say then?'

'I say I'm very sorry but it's quite impossible. And if they press for a reason, I say the same thing about the reason—I'm very sorry but I cannot give it you.'

'Right. I'll try your stone-wall method to-morrow. But I wish it were over.'

It was Thursday morning. John had said good-bye to the family after supper the night before and left very early with only Cap'n Vivian to see him off. There was a general feeling of flatness about every one, and Mary kept the children busily at their lessons. It was not till midday that Tony found a chance to speak to her alone.

'How did he take it, Mary?'

'Badly. How desperately I wanted to fling my arms round him, and shake him into common sense.'

'I wish you had.'

'It's no good. A man must do it himself; he must be master, or he is no use to a woman.'

'How did it end then?'

'He looked so wretched that I tried to pull things down to the commonplace by asking where he would be going next.'

'Poor fellow! That must have been the *coup de grâce*.'

'I'm afraid it was. "Me?" he said, "I'm going to hell",
deadly quietly, and went out of the room.'

Another conversation, between father and mother, occurred that night:

'I didn't like John's look when he went off this morning.
Has Mary treated him badly?' said Cap'n Vivian.

'I'm afraid so. She has been indulging in one of her fits
of caprice, I expect.'

'If so, they'll patch it up all right—lovers' quarrels, you
know, and all that. Can't send John a word, can you?
He's a splendid young fellow.'

'No, I will never lift a finger to push on or hinder anybody's love affairs. But I wish Mary were not so headstrong.'

'Headstrong—a funny word. If it means strong in the
head, I'll back Mary's judgement any day.'

'Her judgement—yes, but not her self-will.'

FIVE

EXPECTANT CURAE

§ I

expectant curae catenatique labores,
gaudia non remanent sed fugitiva volant.
non est, crede mihi, sapientis dicere ' vivam ',
sera nimis vita est crastina: vive hodie.

SOME two months later Tony happened to be at the side
door when the postman came. He handed her a parcel
addressed to herself from Halifax. Guessing it to be from
John, she slipped it under her apron and ran up to her
bedroom, where she could look at it undisturbed. It was
the album that John had shown them. At first glance it
was much the same as before, with most of the pages blank.
The packet also contained a long letter, which Tony was
about to open when her eye caught some writing in the
book which was unmistakably Mary's. She was astounded
to read these lines:

> *Though clouds across the sky are driven*
> *We know the stars at last will shine,*
> *And like the very light of heaven,*
> *I trust thy love. Trust thou in mine.*

What awful poetry, thought Tony, what sentimental stuff!
Mary must have been pretty far gone to have written that.
The more she stared at it the worse it seemed. She feared
that Mary must actually have invented the lines, for no
one could have published them; and there they were,

dated 'Reskadinnick, June 25th'. No doubt poor John had treasured the sentiment, however vile the poetry. His own contributions to the book were bad enough, the later ones full of misery at the loss of her love—too painful to read twice. But the following lines brought tears to her eyes, for the handwriting was not so elegant, and the drawing of his vessel was left only just begun, as if he had not had the heart to finish it:

It was my strongest passion and my first,
It was my first, and it will be my last.
'Twas like the light which on the young world burst
And animated chaos. Yet how fast
The fleeting visions of my Boyhood passed
Into the grave of Time, and taught me how
Futile all our longings!

Then she turned to the letter. As she expected, it was full of heart-broken outpourings, begging Tony to write to him from time to time, and tell him everything she could about her sister. If she were ill or unhappy from any cause at all, and also, yes, if she were married, happily or unhappily, would Tony hide nothing from him? He would keep her posted with his address as he moved about. As for the manuscript book, would she keep it, and give it to Mary at some time when she thought best? If ever Mary should be in trouble . . . the letter trailed off.

Tony vowed that she would do exactly as he said. Oh, why couldn't they have been happy together, she thought, and yet at the back of her mind was the conviction that Mary's judgement had been right.

Every kind of expression from John had called down blessings on Mary, but they might have been curses from the troubles that beset the whole family after he had gone. It soon became known, in that mysterious way that country people manage to hear their neighbours' business, that the affair between John and Mary was at an end. Consequently the demand for her hand became as insistent as before. Very sore and troubled about John, she had no mind for inferior fish, and snubbed every suitor mercilessly. Her spirits were high as ever, but lacked the light gaiety of earlier days. Her parents made no comments and asked no questions. Their anxiety was soon to be turned in another direction, and Mary's troubles were relegated to the 'mercifully over' stage, for serious trouble after John's departure, and in a quite different way, she definitely had had.

An ill fate seemed to attend the younger boys of the family. William, the eldest, was always in splendid health, and had recently married and gone to live in Surrey. But the second boy had died when little more than a baby, and the third, Nicholas, had been drowned when only a few years old, in one of the garden ponds when playing by himself. When the next boy arrived soon after this distress, he seemed to be heaven-sent in consolation, and was named Nicholas. Heaven-sent he continued to seem, beloved by every one more and more as he grew older, and wise beyond his years. His great ambition, as he had shown when a small boy, was to be a doctor, and he spent a great part of his holiday-time from school in the surgery in Camborne. The doctor liked to have him, for he was often able to do some first-aid work in the frequent accidents in the mines.

Tony and he were next in age, and great friends. Into her ears he poured all his ambitious ideas of saving life and limb, restoring injured sight and hearing. 'London, Tony, London,' he would exclaim; 'if only I can get up to London to study I'll learn no end, and you shall help me in my surgery when I start work down here.' He was greatly interested in the cures described in the Gospel, and declared Jesus to have been just a splendid doctor, mostly, he argued, by cheering people up and getting them to heal themselves. 'After all,' he urged in reply to Tony's vague protest, 'what better could any one be? Far more dignified than sitting on a throne somewhere and being worshipped, isn't it?'

On the advice of the Camborne doctor, who had seen a good deal of his natural ability, Nicholas was sent to London to be a student at Guy's. The arrival of his letter home every week was the occasion for a family assembly in the front kitchen, where Cap'n Vivian would read aloud all the accounts of life in the hospital, of the marvellous operations and their results, of simply miraculous new ways of avoiding pain (and even feeling), of inspiring lectures in anatomy from his tutor, a Dr. Gull, and also of jolly recreations with his fellow students. Every letter ended with some reference to his hopes of putting his new ideas into practice down in Cornwall among the miners.

One morning, ever black in the annals of Reskadinnick, a message came that gave Cap'n Vivian no time or desire to call the usual family gathering. Without any previous warning of Nicholas being ill it was a summons from the hospital for his parents to come at once, for their son was suffering from peritonitis, and was on the danger list.

'Get ready at once, Nancy, while I tell Sammy to bring the carriage round, and tell Mary to come too.'

'Can't Tony come as well?'

'No. She had better be left to look after things.'

In half an hour they were off, Tony pressing messages on Mary to take to her beloved brother. The miserable journey was a blank in Mary's memory, but she never forgot the scene in the hospital. There was no chance for messages, or even for recognition of those around him. He lay apparently unconscious, while they watched for the end which they were told was inevitable. At last his eyes opened, his face lit up, and they heard him say, 'I see Jesus coming to meet me', and there was a smile on his face as he died. Grief for him was almost as great in the hospital as in his family. So brilliant a student had he been that he was honoured by burial under the Chapel, in the same vault with the founder, Guy, and Sir Astley Cooper, the famous surgeon, who had died a year or two before.[1] Among the hospital authorities who pressed forward to show their sympathy with his relations was the Dr. Gull of whom he had spoken so often in his letters. Coming back with them to their hotel after the funeral he introduced his sister, with whom he lived, and begged that Mary would come and spend a short time with them before returning to Cornwall. Her parents persuaded Mary to accept the invitation and this visit was the beginning of a long friendship.

[1] The inscription, ' Nicholas Dunkin Vivian. Died 1 Feb. 1846. Aged 20 years ', had become almost obliterated when recent repairs were carried out, and the tomb was removed from its original position. But in a record of the Hospital it is stated, in referring to the Crypt under the Chapel, that ' The latest tomb is that of a student named Vivian, who died in 1846.'

Tony was inconsolable. Neither the honour paid to Nicholas by the hospital, nor the account of his dying words, nor all the appreciation of his work that Dr. Gull had shown, made any impression on her. Death, she said, was death, and there was no getting away from it. Those glorious hopes, all to end in such a fruitless way—there was something wrong with the world.

§ 2

No doubt it is a good thing that troubles never come singly. A fresh one at least takes some of the attention from the others, and leaves no time for brooding on the cruelty of fate. The next one of the battalion that assailed Reskadinnick came from a most unexpected quarter. From Lizzie, of all people. Lizzie was the eldest of the younger part of the family, and was almost as much out of Mary's tutorial hands as Joe, who had been sent away to school. She was distinguished from the rest of the family by her excessive conscientiousness. Thus, for instance, she made a point of mending her stockings regularly, not only the holes, but even the thin places. She spoke so much of duty that the others felt they would rather do anything else. Mary had been able to do nothing with her in the realms of history and literature, although she would read and learn by heart anything that was set her. The piano she practised so assiduously that all life went out of it. She was often shocked at the levity of those around her, and especially that of the parson of Penponds, who enjoyed his game of croquet and his glass of port and his frequently unseemly jokes with Cap'n Vivian far more than spending his time on his sermons. Lizzie's perpetual attitude of disapproval, expressed in words or looks, made her the 'odd man out' of the family, and popular with none of the young men of the neighbourhood. Perhaps because of this she struck out a line of her own, and took to non-conformity. Here she made her own circle of friends, walking off to services at strange hours, with several hymn-books and compressed lips.

'I wish Lizzie would fall in love with some one,' said Tony, 'it would cheer her up. I feel so sorry for her, taking her religion so deadly seriously.'

'Oh, that's only a passing hobby,' said Mary. 'She'll wake up all right. I simply can't imagine any one making love to her. He'd be a stout fellow! I only hope she won't have such a rough awakening as I had.'

Mary had certainly gone through an experience in which she touched bottom, but poor Lizzie had a worse fate in store—she was to flounder in the deep for years and years. It came about in this way:

She received an invitation to a large party given by a prominent Wesleyan. Nothing so worldly as a dance, of course, but 'music and games'. Mary and Tony insisted on Lizzie's buying a new frock to go in and took her to Truro for the express purpose. They did her hair for her in a different fashion from the plastering-down she usually gave it, and made her quite presentable, for she had good features, lacking only animation and humour. Tony drove with her to the door of the house and gave her hearty injunctions to enjoy herself as much as possible; her parting words were: 'Now mind you have a fling, dear. Let yourself go.'

A young man at the gathering, the son of a leading member of the Chapel, thought Lizzie looked pretty, and after she had had a glass of wine, and he several, he thought she was dashed pretty. He told her so, and stole a kiss behind a curtain. This improved her appearance still more, and he ventured an offer of marriage. To say she accepted would be understating the case. She went home truly intoxicated with excitement and a first taste of 'sin'. The next day she announced to every one that she was going to be married.

'Wait a bit,' said her father. 'Not so fast, my dear. I must have a look at this Mr. Reynolds and find out something about him before I give my consent. We'll see.'

Conversation with his wife a few days later was on these lines:

'I've been making inquiries about that young fellow that Lizzie's so crazy about. The results are not too good!'

'She has been talking to me a lot about him—mostly how good he is—that he is a regular chapel-goer, and a strict teetotaller. That seems all right, as far as it goes.'

'As far as it goes, yes. But it doesn't go far enough for my taste. I hear that he carries a flask of "cold tea" in the hunting-field, and smells of brandy.'

'Oh, Joe, I don't like that.'

'Beyond that, and the fact that he has no settled work and is damned ugly, I have nothing against the man.'

'Ugly, is he? You have seen him, then?'

'Had a glimpse of him to-day. He was pointed out to me just as he was going into Tyack's Hotel—for a glass of lemonade, no doubt.'

'What can we do about it?'

'Don't tell me, Nancy, that you are going to keep me from

putting a stop to this silly nonsense—as you did in Mary's case—if only I had put my foot down——'

'Hush, Joe dear, we agreed never to mention that.'

'Anyhow, I mean to stop *this*.'

'But "stopping" a thing like that often makes it worse. My idea is this: *agree* to the match, but postpone its being made a formal affair till she is a little older—that's only reasonable. Then rub Lizzie's nose in it, let her see him drunk if possible. He would probably be very disgusting and offensive, and shock her.'

'What! Have that little rat about the place? No, Nancy. Your scheme is sound, but I couldn't stand it.'

A stormy meeting followed between Lizzie and her father. He told her that anything like an engagement was out of the question, and why. Amid her angry protests and tears he forbade her to ask Reynolds to come to see her, and forbade her to meet him anywhere else. Softening at the end of his harangue, he said: 'Cheer up, Lizzie dear, you have always been a good girl, and I know you will understand and agree to what father and mother, and I am sure your elder sisters, all feel is best for you.'

The next news was that Lizzie had eloped, and was Mrs. Reynolds. Mary hoped that they hadn't actually been married, but they had. The bitter part of it to Cap'n Vivian was the undercurrent of absurdity in the whole affair, and the wound to his dignity. Although none of his acquaintance dared mention it to him, their thoughts came through. To her mother and Tony came the prevision of the lingering life of misery that threatened Lizzie. 'I never knew any good come of a runaway marriage,' Nancy maintained, but

Tony thought that it might be all right in some cases, 'but not with such parents as we have, mother darling'.

These parents began to look at their next daughter with watchful eyes. Emily was a complete contrast to Lizzie, graceful and merry, a blend of Mary's good looks and Tony's lovableness, fond of reading and music, but still fonder of long rides with her brother Joe, when he was at home from school. In their tasks together Mary found her more a companion than a pupil, and she used to follow Tony about in dairy, kitchen, and yard, eagerly learning all she could.

'We shall have no trouble with Emily, anyhow,' was the constant reflection of both parents.

No more trouble, certainly, did they have, except the worst. After a brief illness that no one understood, Emily died. In those days of country life with little or no doctoring, death was a frequent visitor. The weaklings fell while the robust appeared to grow stronger by their reaction to austerities. Like Mithridates, they died old. Thus in this one family three of the five boys died young, but William lived to a hundred, and Joe to ninety.

Nancy was a Christian in the best sense. Her simple, clear-cut creed was that life was good, and that the only real sin was to be miserable. Whatever the disaster, she sucked comfort from the fact that it might have been worse. The happy death-bed of Nicholas partly atoned to her for his loss. When Lizzie made a fool of herself she was able to name a still worse man who it might have been. But in Emily's death she could descry no 'mercy' of any kind, though she made brave attempts. She was more drawn to

Tony at this crisis than ever before. Tony let fly at Providence even more outrageously than she had done when
Nicholas died. 'Providence indeed!' she exclaimed. 'I don't
think much of its provision.' Nancy was shocked at herself
when she realized how far more bracing was Tony's attitude
than the pious consolations poured on her by friends and
cousins in the neighbourhood.

Surely it is a difficult point to decide which is a greater
tragedy and which a less. While the death of Emily plunged
them all in grief, a distress of quite another kind was being
endured unnoticed under the same roof.

From his early childhood Joe had a passion for the sea,
and it became an understood thing that he was to enter the
Navy. His visit to Norway had increased his knowledge of
sea-faring as well as his love of it. His friendship with
Theodore Theiste had been assiduously kept up; this young
sailor had come to Reskadinnick on several visits, always
with fresh interests and voyages to tell about. There was
no doubt as to Joe's ability to pass into the Navy. He had
been sent away to school, but he always said that he had
never been taught anything by any one but Mary. The
necessary mathematics (of which Mary was quite innocent)
Joe managed to work at by himself, with some help from
William or Nicholas. The visit of John, with his stories
and his uniform and his friendly encouragement, had put
a final glory to his dreams. He would be in the Navy;
he would outshine Theodore in the Merchant Service.

Joe knew that there was a limit of age for entering the
Navy, but gave little heed to it, supposing that his father
would be sure to be careful about it. However, a chance

remark of Mary's at breakfast one morning, as to how tall
Joe was getting, made Cap'n Vivian give a start and say,
'When was your birthday, Joe? November 11th? Yes, I
must write for your entrance papers.'

A few days later he took Joe aside and said, 'I hope you
won't be very disappointed, my boy, but my application
was just a month too late. You have exceeded the age limit
for the admission of cadets.'

Joe fought his tears. 'But, father, can't you say it was only
by mistake that you forgot?'

'I'm afraid, my boy, that a rule is a rule. If they made an
exception for you, there would be a grievance with other
people. But I'll write again and say all I can.'

Another few days of wretched suspense passed for Joe,
and then his father summoned him again.

'This letter I have now received says that you can enter
the Navy, after three years' sea-going training, as Master's
Mate in the Navigating Branch. But this entry gives no
opportunity of rising to the rank of Port Captain.'

'Never mind, father. I should be in the Navy, anyhow.'

'I'm afraid it's not good enough, my boy.'

Again and again Joe begged to be allowed to go to sea
in any kind of capacity—he would make his way—Navy or
Merchant Service—it didn't matter. But Cap'n Vivian was
firm, insisting that before long a better career would offer
itself, some position abroad perhaps, something more honor-
able for this his last boy.

These pale half-hopes ended in Joe's taking over the
management of the farm, marrying, bringing up a family,
and living in uncomplaining 'contentment' till he was over

ninety. Day after day, year after year, he rode about the farm on a horse that seemed part of himself and required little or no direction. Always maintaining a slow pace, whether on foot or on horseback, he held his head at a careless angle, with his dreamy eyes on the horizon. He, of all the children of Reskadinnick, certainly led the least adventurous life, and yet was the one who would have given his right hand for a life of excitement and danger. It was not Death who won the game on the spectre bark.

SIX

VIVE HODIE

GLOOM could never settle on Reskadinnick for long. The almost boyish delight that Cap'n Vivian took in all his surroundings infected the whole place and all who came to stay there. If any one commiserated with him on bad times, he would rub his hands joyfully and say, 'Ah, yes, bad they are, but they are going to be much worse—so why not be cheerful while we can?' His family knew him well, and were not taken in by his sham tales of woe.

'Here am I, dead beat,' he would come in with, collapsing in a chair. 'I've toiled all the way from Beacon Hill, all along Basset Road, all the way down Fore Street, all through Blackberry Lane, past the white gate, and all along the drive.'

'Why, father, that's no more than walking home from Camborne!'

'Yes, I know,' he would laugh, 'but I should like a glass of cider and a slice of seedy-cake nevertheless.'

One lovely morning towards the end of April '51 the trees and birds were at the top of their form, and it was Tony's birthday—always a bit of an 'occasion' in the family. But Cap'n Vivian came down with lowering brow, and no sign of a greeting to her. Selecting one of the fiercest chapters in the Old Testament prophets for the usual family prayers, he rolled it forth impressively, and then proceeded to read the Reflections that were tacked on to every chapter in his huge Bible. These were never exhilarating. Breakfast had hardly begun when he looked round the table with a scowl and announced, with pauses for thoughtful appreciation in his hearers: 'Tin has gone down again—I have dismissed George, we can do with two gardeners—I mean to sell a couple of horses.'

'Oh, which ones, father?' from Mary.

'Perhaps, Nancy, you could manage without one of the indoor servants?'

'Yes, easily. Now Fan has gone to school Mary can take on the lamps and the silver. It's really a good thing in a way—she's always happier when she's hard at work, aren't you, Mary?'

'The right spirit, Nancy. We'll all work like niggers. But I fear tin may go down still lower, and things get more restricted. So my idea is that we have a holiday first—make merry beforehand so as to be stronger for the push. I have still a few pounds left. It's Tony's birthday, isn't it?'

'Oh *yes*, father, we thought you had forgotten it.'

'Not at all.' Here he issued a broad grin. 'My idea is a trip up to London—to see this Exhibition they talk so much about. What do you say to it, Nancy?'

'It's a splendid idea. You take the two girls. I can manage at home without them quite well for a week or two, and it will be a pleasant change for me to be rid of you all for a bit. But I won't dismiss one of the servants till you come back.'

'No, nor when we do. That was all nonsense. But I'm afraid, Joe, that you can't go with us. You are wanted too badly just now on the farm.'

Tony was all for staying at home with her mother, but

every one insisted that if she would go and be born in April she must expect when she grew up to be taken to London for the Season.

'Settle what you like,' said Cap'n Vivian, 'but we start in time to be up for the first day, because the Queen is to open the Exhibition in person.'

It soon became evident that it was the journey rather than the Exhibition that was attracting Cap'n Vivian. He was arranging to take the coach only as far as Plymouth, because he was anxious to see the working of the new South Devon railway, connecting Plymouth with Exeter. It was on this line that Brunel had tried out his idea of an atmospheric railway, running the train by compressed air, without using steam at all.

'Not much in it, but still, you never know, and I should like to see some of the apparatus, if it is still there.'

Mary and Tony were more absorbed in going over their wardrobe, to see what would do for London. Mary could be trusted to select the right things for both.

'They taught you how to dress well at school, anyhow,' said Tony, as she watched Mary holding up various items of clothing, scrutinizing, passing, and rejecting, but mainly rejecting with a disgusted look.

'They didn't pay much detailed attention to it,' said Mary, 'but it was impressed on us that to be "bien chaussée" was the main thing—"look after shoes and gloves, and the rest will look after itself".'

Tony spent most of the time arranging the housework so that her mother should have as little bother as possible while they were away. But Nancy appeared so merry at the thought of having the place to herself for a bit after they had gone, that Tony ran up to encourage Mary, who was sitting in her bedroom amid the ruins.

'Mother doesn't seem to mind our going at all—you should hear her.'

'I know,' said Mary, 'she has tried to take me in, too. The lady doth protest too much, methinks.'

'Perhaps I had better stay at home after all.'

'Don't be silly, Tony, the main idea is to give you a holiday, and mother would be more worried if you didn't go. So let's be merry, and please her that way.'

No one would have supposed in seeing Cap'n Vivian starting off with his two daughters that it was a party to mark the occasion of a drop in tin. Tony threw to the wind all her anxieties about the house and Joe's being left behind, as soon as they had started, and Mary was clearly out for a spree.

A fellow passenger on their coach-drive to Plymouth was surprised at their patronizing the new railway. 'You are missing one of the loveliest runs in the kingdom, across the moorland of Devon.'

'Yes,' replied Mary, 'my sister and I are familiar with the route.'

'It's all very well,' said Tony when they reached Plymouth and were in the hotel for the night, 'for you to talk of knowing the coach drive, but the last time you and I came along it we were drenched. It must be a glorious run in good weather.'

When they went to the railway station next morning Tony's comments continued:

'A drive behind a fine team of horses would be so exhilarating over the moors. And far safer than these railway carriages—stuffy little things. At any moment they may run off these gimcrack lines. In fact, I never can see how they stick on at all. And then the engine may blow up, and where should we be?'

'In the sea, most likely,' said Mary, 'for according to father we go quite close to it.'

Tony was only pretending to be nervous of accidents; what she really longed for was a run behind the freshening sou'-wester, which the horses would try to outrace. However, there was plenty to look at in the station. Cap'n Vivian was taken up entirely with his inquiries about the atmospheric experiment, and looking at some of its machinery still to be seen. Curiously dressed and nervous lady-passengers provided scope for Mary's caustic remarks. Luggage labels showed that many of them were 'going to London to see the Queen'. It was a long time before the train started, although Cap'n Vivian had found a carriage for them and settled them in. He himself was to go in another carriage with an engineering friend he had come across. Presently he came once more to their door with a joke he had just heard: 'A ticket-collector on this line has a fine sense of social distinctions. To the third-class passengers he shouts, "Tickuts" at their window. To the seconds he says, "Tickets, please". To the firsts he minces, "Tickits if you please, ladies and gentlemen".'

They were off at last, and all went well, except that they had to keep both windows shut; for every now and then a gust of soot would be blown in. Tony gave a meaning look at Mary, but refrained from comment. At every station most of the men got out for a look round and criticism of the line. Cap'n Vivian was pressing on his acquaintance the possibility of such a line in Cornwall, though how and where the railway would get *into* Cornwall he couldn't see, nor how it would manage to cross the deep valleys when it had got in.

After a while a shower of rain began, and when it turned into a steady downpour Mary exclaimed triumphantly, 'Now aren't you glad that we are cosily in here instead of in the coach, with father getting drenched outside, and the poor horses straining up the hills or slipping and slithering down them?'

She had hardly spoken when the train came to a standstill. Surely not another station already?

'I hope they are coming to ask for the tickets,' said Tony, 'and we shall hear that absurd man.'

'Nonsense, it's no joke, something must have gone wrong,' and Mary opened the window on the lee-side and craned out. She saw her father with a group of other men looking at the engine. Presently he came up to her carriage.

'It's all right. There's a bit of an incline here and the wheels are slipping round without biting. They're sending for some gravel to put down. We shan't be long.'

'There!' said Tony, 'engines can slip and slither as well as horses, and apparently want a lot of time and attention before they can get on again. I like to be behind a creature that has some sense of its own.'

After they had started again the storm increased, and by the time they had reached the coast beyond Teignmouth the stiff sou'wester was lashing up the high tide against the windows.

'Whatever's this?' cried Tony, as she caught up her feet on to the seat. 'The waves are coming into the carriage.' The tide was certainly making a wash over the floor, but the girls kept dry by keeping up on the seat. Their amusement at the adventure was greatly increased by the sound of screams from the adjoining compartment. Mary hoped that the female with the pink frills on her petticoat was getting a thorough wetting; the sea would have then done two good deeds—taught her not to travel in her best dress, and destroyed that pink petticoat.

As they were approaching Exeter the sun shone out, and Mary exclaimed: 'Well, we've been through perils by land and sea, with many a jerk and many a shock, and we are quite filthy; but think of the time we have saved.'

'Really?' said Tony, with all the sarcasm she could muster, 'What, then, is that?' and she pointed to the road where the coach from Plymouth could be seen careering along into the town.

The run to London on the Great Western was easy after this, like a canter after an uneasy trot, as Mary expressed it. Their brother William met them and took them to the rooms he had engaged for them. There had been some difficulty in getting them, for London was crowded with people from all parts. The opening of the Exhibition exceeded their highest expectations, in the crowds of people in the latest fashions, in the endless number of stalls and goods from every imaginable region, even Greenland, and above all in the appearance of the young Queen. She was dressed in white, and looked the picture of pride and happiness. Tony thought there was something pathetic in the mere completeness of her happiness in her husband and in the loyalty of her people.

'Don't get poetical, Tony, and foreboding. She is the luckiest woman in the world.'

'I know a luckier one,' thought Tony.

They were more interested in the people than in the stalls, and were continually inquiring who the obviously important ones were. Mary made friends with a kindly-looking official, who was quite pleased to answer her eager questions. It was thrilling to be so close to Lord Palmerston, but both girls were disappointed that he had no straw in his mouth.

'Who is that nice-looking little girl by the side of the Queen?' asked Mary on the second morning.

'That is the Princess Royal.'

'Oh, of course, why, she is the one that our vessel was named after when we came home from Norway. And who is the young man talking to her now?'

'That is the young Prince from Germany. They say——'

'Never mind the big-wigs, girls,' interrupted Cap'n Vivian. 'William and I must go to have a look at the place where they are showing stamps for crushing ore—may be very useful to us. Mind that you and Tony keep within hail of us—it won't do to get lost here.'

On their way they came upon a crowd of sight-seers round the new Great Western engine, the *Lord of the Isles*. It was very impressive, and among the ecstatic remarks going on around her, Mary recognized the voice of an old schoolfellow of Bath. This girl had married a Frenchman and was now called Mme Costello. She introduced her husband, and after a short chat Mary was invited to return with them to Paris for a few days' visit. Tony urged her to accept, and when Cap'n Vivian was appealed to, he thought it would be a splendid change for her. As they had to go back to Paris the following day, Mary could stay with them a week and be in London again in time for the return to Cornwall. Tony drew Mme Costello aside and said in an undertone, 'Make it as cheery a time as you can. Mary won't mention it, but she had rather a bad shock a few years ago, and we're all trying to make her forget it.'

A nod of comprehension showed that the hint was taken, and the following day Mary was carried off to Paris and shown all the places of historical interest and amusement that the Costellos could think of. Mme Costello's idea of fulfilling her promise to Tony was to hurry Mary to as many places as she could in the time. One that remained longest in her memory was the Sainte Chapelle. It was a sunny morning and the colours in the windows caught her breath with their splendour. Bits were pointed out to her that had been put up when St. Louis built the Chapel; then she realized as never before that Joinville's story was about some one who actually walked the streets of Paris like herself.

Excitement in Paris during her visit was heightened by a revolution going on. Mary, on hearing the word, hoped for the worst, and expected to see a *Carmagnole* at least. But she had to be content with general yeastiness about Louis Napoleon.

'My dear, we think nothing of these things,' said Mme

Costello. 'Indeed, Paris would seem quite dull if some kind of revolution weren't going on.'

'What sort of a man is this Napoleon?' asked Mary.

'Nobody knows. That's the attraction. They say that his hat doesn't know what's in his head.'

A chance remark of Mary's one morning in a restaurant led to another small excitement. M. Costello was grumbling at some item on the menu.

'But it's so easy to take or to leave, as Becky Sharp said.'

'Oh, do you know Becky Sharp? You have read *Vanity Fair*?' said Mme Costello.

'Yes, my sister and I admire Mr. Thackeray so much. He is such a change after the wedding-bell stories. His work is more like real life, when people go and marry the wrong people,' she added with awkwardness and a sudden flush.

Mme Costello noticed her manner and quickly went on, 'You would admire him still more if you met him. I know him well, and find him perfectly charming to talk to—so full of humour. Would you like to meet him? He happens to be in Paris just now. In fact I caught sight of him in the Place de la Concorde as we were driving through yesterday.'

'How could I meet him?' asked Mary eagerly.

'I'll send a note round to ask him to *déjeuner* to-morrow; he'll come if he can, I know, and he isn't likely to be engaged early in the day.'

There came a ready and cordial acceptance by word of mouth through the messenger who took the invitation. Mary spent all her odd moments in the meantime in thinking up points she would ask him, especially about Amelia, whom she and Tony detested. But on the following morning came a pencil scrawl from him, written in bed, excusing himself from coming, 'because I've got such a nedache'. Mary felt that this little note would be a treasure almost compensating for his failure to come, but no imploring would induce Mme Costello to part with it.

The next day was the last of the visit, and a Sunday. Mary suggested that it would be a good thing to go to church.

'Oh yes,' said Mme Costello, 'of course we will. We'll go to *all* the churches.'

They visited so many that Mary was quite confused, for as soon as they had had a brief look round in each one, off they went to another. Before leaving the last one to return home, Mme Costello whispered, 'Like to say a little prayer?'

Mary could only hurriedly decline and laugh to herself to think how shocked her mother would be at this idea of 'going to church' in Paris.

When the time came for Mary to start back to London, Mme Costello couldn't resist the question, 'How is it you have not married? We used to say at school that Vivian would be the first of us to go.'

'Well, the truth is, I've not yet met any one I really care for. I've had some chances, now and again, but . . .'

'Of course you have. But look out, or you may end by being an old maid.'

'I intend to be. I shall never marry.'

'Good! People who say that are certain victims.'

Mary laughed in a hearty, carefree way. Apparently she had nothing in the romantic, broken-hearted line to disclose or to hide. And yet, thought Mme Costello, her sister had distinctly hinted at *something*.

Cap'n Vivian met Mary at Dover. He had come by himself, he explained, because he wanted a chat with her, and the journey to town would give him an opportunity.

'Nothing dreadful happened, I hope, father?'

'No, dear, on the contrary. Who do you think has come over for the Exhibition? Otto Barnholt. He with Yetta and Sophie appeared on the scenes the very day you went away. They went to the *Lord of the Isles*, feeling sure that I should be there, if anywhere, sooner or later.'

'How splendid for Tony.'

'Yes. I rather think she must have let him know we were coming. Of course, Otto didn't say he had come over to see her,' said Cap'n Vivian with a twinkle of his eye, 'He persuaded his father that some rival timber firms would be having some exhibits, and that some one ought to have a look round for ideas and so on. Besides (always suspect a 'besides') it would be a great thing for the girls to see London at such a time, when everything would be at its best—shops and all those things women like.'

'I don't care what reasons he gave so long as he has come, and will be with Tony.'

'And I've persuaded them all three to come down to Cornwall with us. We have only been waiting for you to come back. We shall start home as soon as possible.'

'Any other news?'

'Yes. You will be glad to hear that William is taking Lizzie's husband into partnership with him, and they are all going to live together in his house in Surrey.'

'All your news seems good. No sign of a child for William yet, I suppose?'

'No, we can hardly expect it after these years. It's Tony we must look to for our first grandchild. With ten children born to one, it seems hard not to have a grandchild, doesn't it?'

'Perhaps Lizzie?'

'God forbid! With that scoundrel of a husband.'

'Rather harsh language, father, isn't it? He may not be so bad as we fancy—if only he is good to Lizzie.'

'Ah, that is the very thing I wanted to talk to you alone about. William has told me an ugly little story of something that occurred a little while ago in the Reynolds's house in London. There was a girl staying with them—I don't know who it was—and one night the three of them sat up rather late. Lizzie was wishing to goodness that the visitor would propose going to bed. At last, after several hints, Lizzie said she was sorry but she was too tired to sit up any longer, and begged to be excused. She went up to bed, but wasn't happy at having left her visitor like that, and couldn't get to sleep. After about half an hour she was aware that the door-handle of the bedroom was being quietly turned. She then saw that it was her husband carrying a candle. 'He is being careful not to disturb me,' thought she, but some instinct or whim induced her to pretend to be sound asleep. Instead of undressing for bed, he came close to her, and stood for some time watching her intently. She managed to keep up her pretence of sound sleep, although, poor child, her heart was pounding. What was he wanting? She soon knew. He turned and stealthily went downstairs again.'

'Poor little Lizzie,' cried Mary, 'How could she bear it? But the wonder to me is that she could ever tell any one.'

'She confided in William because there was no one else within reach, and she was too worried to say anything or to take any action herself. Of course dear old William said at once that he would horsewhip the scoundrel.'

'Yes, yes, and I hope he did.'

'No. Lizzie so implored him to forget it, and do his best for them both, that William was melted and out of sheer pity for Lizzie and anxiety to protect her, proposed this joint household arrangement.'

'It seems to me a bit risky. How does William's wife like the idea?'

'She will be glad of Lizzie's company. It's quite another risk that I'm thinking of. I hope William won't let him have free control of the money in the business.'

'I suppose any crookedness in that direction is almost as bad as the other kind of crookedness.'

'Worse, my dear. One can forgive sudden temptations and so on; passion comes and goes, but greed is in the soul, and once a man has played false with money, he is hopeless. Sounds sordid, but it's a fact. I don't mean a sudden theft by a man in a desperate strait—but, Mary, the truth is I don't trust that fellow in any direction at all.'

' "Him being so particler religious, that put Master 'pon 'is guard",' quoted Mary.

'Exactly,' laughed her father, but it was not his usual genial laugh. 'But we'll keep these misgivings to ourselves. It's been a relief to me that you know about them, and I can always rely on your appearing completely ignorant.'

There were no awkward silences in their rooms that evening when the Vivians and the Barnholts had supper together.

'I nearly met Mr. Thackeray,' was Mary's first outburst to Tony.

'We saw Tennyson talking to the Queen,' riposted Tony, and presently added in an undertone. 'Father has let himself in for a big extravagance while you were away; but we'll tell you all about that when we get home—it's a secret, a birthday present for you.'

This was said among confused boastings from the others as to what they had seen, and got for presents to take home. Then Mary took up the tale with an account of the Parisian garments of the most modish that she had bought for her mother and Tony to 'startle Camborne' with. 'Paris is nothing to Regent Street,' argued the Barnholt girls, at which Mary smiled to herself, thinking that they had not yet seen what she had in her trunk.

Cap'n Vivian put up a wry face at the numerous and bulging trunks when it came to starting for Cornwall. The two drivers of the four-wheelers assembled at the door stood looking at them in a discouraged sort of way until Mary harangued them, 'Come, come, my good men, put your backs into it. These trunks are full of good things for the poor and needy. It is thirsty work we know, but Paddington can supply drinks—indeed it is quite notable for them.'

With broad grins the men set to work. And a broad grin was the key-note of that memorable journey, when every one was brimming with happiness, and fully aware of the delight that their arrival would cause at Reskadinnick.

Cap'n Vivian's piece of extravagance in London had arisen from their visit to the Academy. Struck by the workmanship in a portrait by Field Talfourd, he declared that Mary would make a capital subject for the painter, and he had half a mind to get him to paint her portrait, to celebrate her thirtieth birthday. Half a mind with him was as good as a whole one. When Tony expostulated with him about the extravagance, he replied that this jaunt to London cried aloud for a climax.

'This pleasure trip,' said he, 'is like a mince pie, which always calls for a drop of brandy after it.'

So Talfourd was interviewed, and by good chance was to be down in Falmouth during the summer. If Mary could come to him there two or three times for sittings, he could bring in a bit of Falmouth harbour as a background.

Expeditions to Falmouth therefore took on an air of duty, and opened up fresh occasions for sight-seeing and picnics. Mary and Yetta would generally ride ahead, while Joe and Sophie, Otto and Tony brought up the rear. The portrait was a great success and was hung among sundry ancestors in the dining-room. Cap'n Vivian would never tell how much he had given for it. 'These artists, poor devils,' he would mutter, 'deserve all they can get.'

It was confidently expected that Otto and Tony would be married in the following year, and though little was said every one was thinking of it.

'Oh, Tony darling, what shall I do when you go away?' her mother slipped out one day, and then hurriedly added, 'there will be heaps of pleasant jobs to do, and Mary at home to help, and there will be letters from you, with all your *new* interests to tell us about. I'm really longing for it.'

'We won't worry about my going away till I actually go,' replied Tony; 'I haven't gone yet.'

'Oh, Tony darling, what shall I do when you go away?' was Mary's frequent and undisguised lament.

'Don't worry,' Tony would laugh, 'it may be you that will go first.'

SEVEN

TOM

§ 1

When the holiday was over and the Barnholts had
returned to Norway, the family at Reskadinnick had to face
the rather thin time that Cap'n Vivian had foreseen. Ex-
penses had to be curtailed, and each of the children had to
do something towards the general upkeep of the place. Joe
threw all his energy into the development of the farm; the
crops, the animals, and the mill kept his hands full. Tony
was working up a steady income by selling milk, cream, and
butter to the cottagers scattered over the downs. It was
only Mary who no longer had a clear-cut job, now that
there were no young ones to teach. Having a real gift for
teaching, and liking it, she suggested to her father that she
might take a post somewhere as a governess.

'As a what?' he exclaimed in such a horrified tone that
she never dared to approach the subject again. Her mother
was equally firm, if not so violent.

'Besides, dear,' she added, 'when Tony is married, there
will be heaps for you to do here to help me. Besides—— '

'What? Another "besides"?'

'No, darling, there is only one reason, and you know well
enough what it is. We want you here to cheer us up, and
to laugh however bad the news may be.'

So Mary took up the role of helping in each department.
She turned out to be by far the best sempstress in the

family. She explained that she had been taught every possible stitch at Bath, but had kept her knowledge quiet, as she hated the business. Now it came in useful, as her mother's eyes were not what they had been, and the endless tucks required for her father's shirts were a grilling task. As she sat at these hour after hour she determined that if ever she had a daughter she would never force on her any sewing but the barest that was necessary. 'Not that I shall ever have a child of course,' she would reflect.

In the kitchen she was more in her element. Making meals seemed to her much more fun than making and mending clothes and household linen. She did everything in a semi-detached, slap-dash style that rather alarmed Tony. But the results were good—the pastry light, the saffron-cake spongy, the bacon done to a turn, 'cooked with brains' as her father said. She maintained that there was far too much fuss made about cooking.

'The quicker you are, the better the pudding,' she would say. 'Just think of Lizzie.' The letters that came from Lizzie gave the impression that she had spent a whole morning making an apple tart or a lemon sponge.

'I expect she endeavours to attract her husband by dainty dishes,' said Tony. 'I can picture her poring conscientiously over a cookery book. And I shouldn't be surprised to hear that she actually weighs the things.'

Here the two girls laughed as they pictured Lizzie solemnly weighing out three-quarters of a pound of currants, with only a one-pound weight and a half-pound one, and what to do?

Mary, with her hand in every department of the running of the house, soon saw that Tony had too much to do, and must be driven away somehow. There had been repeated invitations from the Barnholts, begging Tony to come over to be consulted about the plans Otto was making for the new house they were to live in. At last Mary took the matter into her own hands, and plotted quietly with her father. In a day or two she was careering down the path across the brook, into the kitchen garden, calling out 'Antonina' as she went. Tony was busy gathering black currants and responded, 'What's the news? You look very pleased.'

'I am. You are starting for Norway for a short visit—early next week.'

'I love a joke, but that one isn't funny.'

'No joke. Father tells me that he has to go off suddenly to Norway, about some timber, and thinks you may as well go too, and put in a flying visit to the Barnholts. I didn't stop for details, but just flew out here to tell you.'

A flush of excitement and then cold doubt beset Tony.

'Father going to Norway! Nonsense—I believe it's all your doing,' and she eyed her sister suspiciously.

'Well, it's a poor heart that never pulls a string or two. Anyhow, everything's planned, and it's no use.'

'But it's impossible. I simply can't leave things.'

'Don't be silly, thinking yourself so important. I know quite well how you do the milk, and feed the fowls and count the turkeys and everything. I've watched you.'

'But Elizabeth is so stupid. She would let the milk burn, and forget to——.'

'Why of course she will. If she were as clever as we are she wouldn't be our servant. But the old place will rock along quite well without you. Don't be so conceited.'

Mary carried her scheme through, but only on one con-
dition from Tony—that she herself would have a holiday
afterwards. The visit to Norway was the more necessary
because Otto's wedding had to be put off on account of his
father's illness. Two hurried visits to Reskadinnick since
the Exhibition year, snatched while his vessel was discharging cargo at Falmouth, had been all that Otto had contrived
during the five years that had passed. Among the many
hot-headed acts of Mary that had to be regretted, this *coup
de famille* came to be remembered by herself and all concerned as one of her happiest ideas.

Tony returned with glowing accounts of the house that
was beginning, and of the heavenly time she had had with
Otto. 'Thank you, Mary, for it was your doing entirely,
and remember this, that if I never have another happy day,
I have had my share of bliss.'

According to plan, Mary's holiday followed. Another
cheery time with the Costellos in Paris, and then a long-
promised visit to the Gulls in London. She came home so
invigorated by the change that Tony hoped to have some
news of an interesting kind.

'Has anything been happening by any chance?' she asked.

'No, no, Tony, have no hopes for me, dear; I'm quite
stony-hearted. But William Gull is a charming man—mainly
I think because he is so wrapped up in his work. He told
me that his ambition is to be Physician in Ordinary to the
Queen.'

'Oh is it! How modest! And what is his sister's ambition?'

'None—unless it be to have an audience. She suffers

from a grievance. I slept in the same room with her, and she talked of nothing else. My advice is, never sleep with a person with a grievance. She would wake in the small hours and begin on it at once.'

'Was it anything very serious?'

'I have no idea. She talked about it so much that I was completely confused. There were as many characters in it as in one of Thackeray's novels, and I lost count. How glad I am to be at home again among the cheerful.'

'It sounds like a Norsk Saga,' said Tony.

'Related by Miss Bates,' added Mary.

'Couldn't you do anything to stop her? I've never known you beaten in the art of shutting people up.'

'I did succeed at last. After some delicate yawning, of which she took no notice, I got desperate. But a good chance was thrown into my lap—unfortunately too near the end of my visit to be of much use. One night she ran on as usual till past midnight with her perpetual "so she said" and "so I said," interlarded with notes of indignation and the dreaded demands "What would you have done in my place?" Sleep, however, comes at last, even to this kind of thing. At about 3 o'clock I woke and couldn't get off again. I looked across at her bed—there she was gently snoring, and a thirst for vengeance seized me. I could have drunk hot blood. I lit my candle, went over to her, shook her awake, looked as agitated as I could, and said "You don't mean to say that she actually spoke to you like *that*?" Quite dazed and clearly annoyed she almost pushed me away with "Never mind now." "But I can't get to sleep for thinking of it," said I; "do tell me now." "I'll tell you in the morning,"

said she: "go back to bed now." I retreated in good order
and shook with laughing under the bedclothes. There was
no renewal of the grievance next day to my internal amúse-
ment; but oh, Tony, I prefer Reskadinnick even in my
mirth.'

§ 2

One autumn evening Mary was up in her room trying to
paint the riot of red and gold of the trees by the lawn,
when Tony's head appeared round the door.

'You might come down for a few minutes, Mary. Father
has brought a young mining-student home with him, and
I'm afraid it looks like his stopping to supper.'

'Another! What a nuisance! I'm so tired of these young
men, all alike, all shy and awkward, and not a word to say.
And look at these colours, aren't they splendid? I did so
want to catch the last of the sunlight for them.'

'Yes, and you have caught something of them,' said Tony
coming to look. 'But do go down, because I've had to leave
mother to do the polite talking, while I get some pasties
into the oven, and make a junket.'

'You go on then. I'll come at once. What's the young
man's name?'

'Most uninspiring—Tom Thomas! But I like his look,
and father has evidently taken a fancy to him, for he already
calls him Tom.'

After a last splash at her tree Mary grudgingly went down
to be as agreeable as she could to one of those dull-witted
students. Our minds seem to have a curious power of retain-
ing every detail of some occasion, commonplace in itself,

and destined to be forgotten among a hundred similar ones, were it not for some strong feeling aroused which acts like a reviving chemical on a faded picture. How vividly Mary always remembered the dazzling colour of those autumn trees, Tony's face at the door, full as usual of cares about everybody but herself, and the subsequent happenings of the evening.

On opening the breakfast-parlour door she saw her mother contentedly knitting in the corner, by a bright log fire. In the light of the large lamp on the table was spread out a big coloured plan, over which her father and the stranger had their heads together, so engrossed that they didn't notice her coming in. There was still a bit of daylight, so thinking she might just as well run upstairs again and do a little more to her painting, she whispered 'back soon' to her mother and was half out of the room again, when her father chanced to look up.

'Don't go away, Mary dear, I want to introduce Mr. Thomas to you. He has only lately come to the Mining School from his home in Wales. This is my eldest daughter, Tom.'

After a brief interchange of opinion on the weather, and hopes that he had found satisfactory lodgings, Mary was well aware that both men were longing to resume their study of the plan, so out of politeness she bent over it and asked what it was about.

'You see, Miss Vivian, I've got an idea, and your father is kind enough to think there are possibilities in it. This is a plan of the projected Cornish Railway. There is talk of linking it up with the line from London to Plymouth.

We may be able to go all the way from London to Penzance by train.'

'They've just opened a grand new terminus at Paddington,' said Cap'n Vivian, 'and I hear that Brunel is planning a bridge over the Tamar, so it looks like business and as if there were money to spend.'

'And what is this idea of yours, Mr. Thomas?' asked Mary.

'It's like this: all the railways that are spreading over the country are obliged to have some *one* place along the line for a repairing-shop. You see they have to store their spare parts, and have sheds for building new engines and repairing any that are damaged.'

'Yes, I see that,' said Mary, 'and I suppose men would have to live there who could do the work.'

'Exactly, and as they need plenty of space for all this, they pitch on some spot in the country, for the terminus is all taken up with the actual traffic.'

'Oh yes, Father, you remember that little place called Swindon, where you told me they were busy with "works".'

'Well now, the point is, where would be the best place for such a workshop on this West Cornwall Railway?'

Mary hung over the map for some time, and then put her finger on Carn Brea. 'Here are the best mines; here are the skilled workmen; here are stores of metal and timber; and here are we!' She looked up with a laugh to see the others laughing too.

'You have hit exactly on Tom's idea. It seems reasonable, but too good to be true. It would bring plenty of profit our way.'

Then followed a discussion of details, and some calculations on paper, with a rough estimate of the large amount of timber that would be required for sleepers and for the viaducts over the valleys.

'The more timber the better,' said Cap'n Vivian, 'for that will bring more trade to Barnholt.'

'That sounds good,' said Tony, as she came in, just catching the last remark. 'More timber wanted from Norway?'

The new ideas were explained to her, and she pronounced them to be very promising, but at the moment supper was still more promising, and would they clear the table for it? Immediately the visitor began to say good-bye to Mrs. Vivian.

'Certainly not,' said she; 'why you have only just begun to know us. My son Joe will be in presently, and he will want to hear all the news. Now if you will hold this wool for me while the girls are seeing to the supper, that will be most kind.'

It was a jolly supper party, for the pasties were done to a turn, and Tony had been lavish with the cream for the junket. Mr. Thomas said he had never enjoyed a meal so much. He told them of some of the primitive ways among the Welsh hills, and specially amused Mary by saying that he had seen in one cottage a piece of wall-paper carefully framed in gilt and hung over the mantelpiece, while a lovely piece of old china was put down for the dog's dinner-bowl.'

'I hope you captured it,' said Mary.

'Yes. I offered to buy it, but the old woman was shocked at such a thing. "Inteet and you shall haf it," she insisted.'

After supper and general leave-taking, Mr. Thomas was

pressed to come again and tell them more about Wales.
'And hear more about your adventures, sir, at sea and
abroad, and *under* the earth. What a glorious life you have
led!' Then correcting himself with a glance round the room
and resting on Mary, '*Are* leading, I mean.'

'What a very pleasant boy!' exclaimed Mrs. Vivian
when he had gone.

'Boy!' said Cap'n Vivian. 'Well, in years I suppose he is
not much more—about twenty-something but he has the
head of a man of forty. He tells me he is the eldest of a large
family, so no doubt he has had to be a bit thoughtful.
Anyhow, he has a shrewder sense of affairs than most of
the fellows I come across.'

'It's a good thing that he has a head for business, but what
struck me about him was his extraordinary——' she hesi-
tated for a word.

'Sunniness? Is that what you mean, mother?' put in
Mary.

'Yes. All the time he was here it was as if the sun were
shining in the room. I can't think why. He didn't talk a
great deal, or make jokes or anything. Did you notice,
girls, how kindly he spoke to me about these terrible reports
from India? "Greatly exaggerated," that's what he said
they were. Most reassuring.'

When the girls were alone together later on that same
evening there was further comment.

'Not a bad sort, was he?' began Tony.

'No,' admitted Mary, 'there is something quite odd about
him, delightfully odd. So debonair. Such an open face.
He looked me straight in the eye without seeming to be

aware that I was a woman. He actually listened to what I said and even disagreed on one point. Oh, Tony, if you only knew how refreshing this is, after all the bowing and blushing and yammering of the young men we generally get!'

'You forget,' laughed Tony, 'that you are a beautiful woman.' (Mary made an impatient gesture.) 'No, wait till I've finished my sentence, a beautiful woman with a very sharp tongue—and a stand-offish manner—I hardly wonder the poor fellows are afraid of you.'

'Afraid! Good gracious! Fancy any one being afraid of *me*!'

'Well, they are, and I expect if Mr. Thomas had not been a new-comer, without a chance of hearing anything about you, he would have been nervous too.'

'Oh, Tony, what an ogre I must be! What am I to do?'

'You must manage to control your tongue, your sense of the ludicrous, and your superior knowledge. No one likes being put right. And after all what does it matter?'

'Yes, but when a young man says "You are a perfect Adonis," how can one help laughing and suggesting a closer study of the story? And believe me they are always wrestling with some dreadful quotation, instead of carrying on a rational conversation.'

'It's the price you pay for being beautiful—you can't have everything.'

'I feel like Mme de Staël, only the other way round. She was ugly and intellectual, and always being extolled for her powers of mind. "I wish," she used to say, "that they would praise me for my beauty, and leave my mind alone."'

'Well, Mary darling, you have both. What more do you want?'

Suddenly Mary burst out, 'Oh, Tony, I've seen you and Otto together and envy you. What I want is to find a man like that, one who would love me madly and treat me like an equal, and not care a button whether I had good looks or brains or anything else.'

'Of course, what woman wouldn't? But you are heavily handicapped for that—as heavily as if you were a poor wealthy heiress. As for me, now, I'm in the fine position of having neither looks nor brains, so Otto can't be disappointed.

'I quite agree that your brain is feeble, or you would know that every mortal creature loves you, you old silly.'

Only a week or so later there was another sisterly conference.

'I've found what I wanted, Tony. Tom loves me right enough, and you must be the first to know it.'

'In that you are correct. I knew it before you did. Being in love yourself makes you pretty quick to detect it in others. My only surprise is that he has taken so long to tell you.'

'Oh, come, it's not a fortnight since he first came.'

'But he has been in nearly every day since.'

'He says he was rather alarmed on his first approach to the house, what with the air of wealth that Reskadinnick gives, and father's grand manner and all, but as soon as he came inside he felt the homely atmosphere of mother and all of us, and completely forgot his shyness.'

'I hope you disabused him of any idea of our wealth.'

'I just laughed at it. "You won't mind living in a small house at first then, and managing a bit?" he said. "Leave me alone for managing," I said. "If you give me five shillings a week to manage on, I'll manage on it," and then I added that if it came to the worst we could go round with a barrel organ.'

'He liked that, didn't he?'

'Yes. "That's the spirit," said he, "but I am young and healthy and make friends easily, and I'm lucky; and you know what Napoleon said about a lucky man." Seizing my chance I broke in here, "Talking of age," said I, "I must tell you that I look a good deal younger than I really am."'

'Ah, what did he say to that?' asked Tony. 'I've been a bit anxious about that, since he is so young.'

'He said that a woman was as young as she looked, or felt, he couldn't remember which it was, nor did he care. At that I executed a *pas seul,* and said I felt like a two-year-old. His response to that I leave to your imagination.'

'Well,' said Tony a bit seriously, 'I suppose difference of age doesn't matter much, but how about that other affair, did you tell him about that?'

'No, and I'm wondering whether I ought to?'

'I shouldn't if I were you. Silence is golden.'

'Yes, but if he should ask some time or other how it was that I had remained unmarried so long, then what?'

'People never ask the things we dread. It's their absolute lack of curiosity that amazes me. And if he should ask, you can put him off as you did Mme Costello. Or you could expand a little about John Symons—or any other of your numerous suitors—in fact tell him anything as long as you don't seem mysterious.'

'Yes, I've found that. As long as you burst out in confidence about something else, people keep off the thing you don't want to tell.'

'I've often wondered why one doesn't tell a direct lie and be done with it. It would be more honest, I think.'

'Mother would faint at the idea of telling a verbal lie, wouldn't she? I suppose it's some "word of honour" idea. There's nothing against it in the Bible so far as I know.'

'Anyhow it's against all our upbringing, and we shall never be able to do it. But take heart, Mary; if by any chance Tom comes to know, he won't mind. If I were told something of the kind about Otto, it wouldn't make the faintest difference to my love for him.'

'Bless you, Tony, you are a rock.'

§ 3

Nearly two years had to go by before Tom was through his mining course, had obtained work, and was able to marry. Meanwhile something of the old gaiety was restored to Reskadinnick, not through social entertainments but merely by the infectious high spirits of Tom and Mary. Although she was fifteen years his senior, she had the appearance of being about the same age, and in her attitude to life she often seemed even younger. No day passed without an exchange of love letters, even when Tom was staying in the house. On the high mantelpiece in the front kitchen was an ancient mug. In this they agreed to place their letters, each contributing a note and abstracting one. They never had any lovers' quarrels, but one morning Mary's love of mischief induced her to pretend to be offended with Tom, and in order to make a little drama of it she placed no letter in the cup. However she couldn't resist having a look at the one for herself; so she took it out, read it, and put it back in the cup. The look on Tom's face when he found his letter next day apparently untouched was not so amusing a surprise as she had anticipated. In fact she was thoroughly ashamed of herself, and hoping for a little merry sympathy she confessed what she had done to Tony. She had her surprise then, for Tony burst into one of her flashes of anger: 'How could you do such a mean trick! To Tom of all people! A sly kind of low school-girl thing to do!——'

'Surely you are making a mountain out of a molehill; it was only a bit of fun.'

'I see no fun in it at all. A man can forgive big things but a petty deception like that sticks in his mind. You did it just to amuse yourself by hurting him. Your caprice will bring trouble some day if you don't look out.'

Mary was too much ashamed to find her usual ready retort, and edged away from the topic by asking if there were any special news from Otto in the letter that had just come. Yes, there was news, a mixture of good and bad. Old Mr. Barnholt had been failing still more in health since his wife's death, and practically all the work had now fallen on Otto's shoulders. The bit of good news was that Theodore Theiste was on his way to England, and due at Falmouth in February. He would be able to explain a great deal more than could be put in a letter.

'That's certainly good news, but I wish to goodness,' said Mary, 'that it was to be Otto himself coming to fetch you. How lovely it would be if we could have a double wedding.'

'A bit hard on mother to lose us both at once,' said Tony, 'but there seems no likelihood of it, if you are to be married this summer.'

Cap'n Vivian was delighted to hear of Theodore's visit. 'I suppose, Joe,' said he, 'that you can be trusted to go to Falmouth to meet Theodore? There must be no running off to sea with him, mind.'

Joe laughed a little ruefully at the idea and said, 'It would take a lot to keep Theodore from his beloved Reskadinnick.'

The trip to Falmouth to meet him was a mixture of bliss and misery to Joe. He was full of pride in his friend, now an important man, respected by his officers and crew. It was a lovely morning, with the first touch of spring in the air, when Joe found him on his vessel, issuing his final orders before leaving. Falmouth was looking its best, and the sight of the shipping, the medley of sounds from the docks, the alluring smell of tar and the inviting breeze— all were too much for Joe. Theodore guessed his trouble and hurried him away, saying that he had only two days to spare, and they had better start for Camborne at once.

Mrs. Vivian regarded Theodore almost like another son, and was always deeply grateful to him for his kindness to Joe. His friendship with Nicholas during a former stay at Reskadinnick was another bond between them. Joe had told him all about Tom on the journey down, so it seemed like a real old family gathering at the supper table on his arrival. Cap'n Vivian was all agog for sea-stories, and as soon as he had served them all round began: 'So I hear you are in command of the *Baron Holberg*—a bit young, aren't you, my boy, for such a responsible position?'

'Oh no, Sir, why I'm over twenty-five!'

Cap'n Vivian looked at his wife and smiled. 'Yes, of course that is a good age, but still, I understand that she is one of the finest ships of Norway's Mercantile Marine. A stroke of luck, surely, for you to have her for your first command?'

'Yes indeed, it was a bit of luck. It came about in this way: a desperate message came to head-quarters in Christiania one day, to say that the *Baron Holberg* was lying in Sydney Harbour, deserted. All hands had left, and the skipper was at his wits' end and was asking for instructions.'

A chorus of questions came from the supper-table. 'Why had they deserted? Did the skipper stay?' 'I bet,' said Tom, 'that it was a plague of some kind; men can stand any danger rather than that.' 'But then the skipper would have run away too,' said Mary. 'Oh no,' said Joe, 'he daren't leave his ship.'

'Be quiet, all of you,' said Cap'n Vivian, 'and let's hear what it was.'

'You are all on the wrong tack' said Theodore, 'it was no fear of anything—it was greed. Just a year or two ago, you remember, gold was discovered out there, and by this time the diggings were in full swing. No sooner had they docked than the news of it spread among the crew, and every blessed man jack of them sloped off. The skipper was obviously a bit of a fool, and instead of attempting to do anything sent that message home, and sat down.'

'But it takes such a time to get the message over. Didn't he do anything at all?' asked Tony.

'Well, you shall hear. When the message reached head-quarters, they applied to Captain Christian Barnholt, asking him to recommend a man who could be sent out at once. He himself was retired of course, and he recommended me, being kind enough to say that I had excellent navigating ability, plenty of courage, and could manage men.'

'He was right there, as I can testify,' said Cap'n Vivian.

'I don't call that luck at all,' put in Tom; 'you were the best man. Do go on.'

'Merely on his recommendation, without any further inquiries of any kind, they sent full instructions to me with a formal written authority, to go out to Sydney, take command of the vessel, get together a crew as best I could, and bring her home.'

'How splendid!' cried Tony; 'but what a job!'

'Yes, it took my breath away for a bit, but they had eased it as much as they could by sending me plenty of money, and telling me not to be sparing. Believe me, I just threw my kit together and started by the very next steamship from Brevig. Luck was certainly with me on the voyage, for I reached Sydney without undue delay anywhere, and to my vast contentment I found the *Baron Holberg* all safe and sound.'

'Any trouble with the skipper?' asked Cap'n Vivian.

'Ah, now that, as you can guess, was exactly what had been my chief worry all the way out. I was mean enough to fear that he had managed to get a crew and was on his way home, and me having to come back with my tail between my legs. That was why I was so overjoyed to see the vessel. You get rid of one worry only to find another waiting round the corner.'

'Yes,' said Joe, 'I'm longing to know what the skipper said to you. That must have been the real worry.'

'For some reason or other I pictured a man with a fierce-looking black beard, who would become very unpleasant at having to give up his command to a mere boy. So all the way on the voyage I encouraged my moustache and frowned as much as possible—don't laugh. The second worry melted like the first. *There was no one there at all.* I gathered from the gossip on the quay that the skipper had gone off to the gold-diggings himself. So not even you were right, Joe.'

'What a relief! What did you do? How did you get a crew?'

'I took my time. There's a time to hurry and a time to be deliberate, I thought. I had hurried out for obvious reasons. But I meant to choose my officers and men very carefully. I wanted the right sort. Day by day, one by one, I found them, on the docks and in the town. One or two had already tried the gold-digging and found it a miserable life, and were looking for a ship homeward bound.'

'Any of the old crew, by any chance?'

'Yes, one man put it forward as a plea to be taken on again. I gave him a bit of my tongue, I tell you; but I guessed that he was genuine, and took him on. I gave them all plenty of work to do on the ship, until we were ready to sail. Almost at the last minute the second mate came to me with a very long face. "What's up now?" I asked, fearing some horrible hitch. "Do you know, Sir, that the man who signed on last night is a Roman Catholic! Whatever is to be done?" "Good God, man," I cried, "be thankful that he is anything at all."'

'And now for the journey home,' said Mary. 'Let's clear the table, Tony, and get the big atlas.'

They crowded round Theodore while he traced his route.

'You surely didn't venture through the Torres Strait?' said Cap'n Vivian; 'I've always understood that to be a difficult bit of navigation.'

'It is, but I had studied the charts on my outward journey, and was longing to try it. It saved time, of course, but it was really vanity on my part. I wanted to impress my officers.'

'Across the Indian Ocean, yes,' said Joe, poring over the map, 'then round the Cape. You got some storms there?'

'Oh yes, a bad storm or two, but she rode them out finely. And how proud I was when we came into Brevig. I reckoned we had done over twelve thousand miles.'

Tony found a chance on the following day to get Theodore to herself, and hear all the latest news about the Barnholts. He was full of the new house that Otto was building for her, which was getting on finely. The workmen were taking a pride in putting their best work into it.

'And who is to live in the big house? Sophie is going to be married soon, isn't she?'

'No. I'm sorry to say that has come to nothing. So Otto is planning for the two sisters to live on together in the big house, within hail of you two; but he can't bear to talk of the time when his father will be gone.'

'I suppose there is no hope of his father's doing much active work again?'

'None. But cheer up, Tony, you and Otto deserve the very best the world can give. I long to see you in that new house. I shall be able to tell Otto how well you are looking. And may I take him a kiss?'

§ 4

Tom and Mary were married in the following June. Mrs. Vivian considered it very merciful that Tony's wedding had been put off for a while.

'It would have been so dreadful, dears, for you both to go into foreign countries at the same time.'

'But Liverpool isn't a foreign country, mother dear,' said Mary. 'We don't even have to cross any water; and people speak English there. It isn't a bit like Norway.'

'From Tom's account it is a long journey, though.'

'However long it is, Tom and I mean to be coming down to see you often and often.'

There had been some demur on the part of Tony and her mother as to whether Mary was wise in being married until Tom had a more substantial income, but Cap'n Vivian backed Mary up in her idea that a struggle with difficulties was far more fun than a comfortable certainty.

'You remember, Nancy, how short we were ourselves when we first set up, and the scanty meals we often had in this very room? And were never quite sure about the next? How we used to laugh when we insisted that we preferred eggs to meat. You thought it was a mercy that we had no child to feed. A short-lived mercy, but a better one was on its heels, wasn't it?'

'Yes, indeed, the grand mercy of William's arrival.'

'With you everything is a mercy.'

'Well, dear, so it is, and I wouldn't have been without

our worst troubles. But somehow one is so much more of a coward for one's children than for oneself.'

'That's true. But Tony's future looks rosy enough, and Mary would be wasted if she hadn't a battle or two.'

Tom had written to say that he had taken a small house in Rainhill, had put some furniture in, and could get a few days from his work. Would Mary be ready to be married and carried off?

Cap'n Vivian thought it must be enjoyable to live in Rainhill, the very place where Stephenson had run his *Rocket*. Mary didn't care in the least where her home was to be, but she was determined that her wedding should be kept as quiet as possible—out of range of friends and relations in Camborne. She knew that it was hopeless to keep anything secret, and was therefore greatly cheered when her brother William suggested that she should be married from his house in Surrey, in the little parish church of Cheam. She and Tony could come to stay for a time beforehand, and Tom could come and carry her off.

William saw to it that his sisters should enjoy the scenery of Surrey during their visit. It was a new type of country to them and was at its very best in the end of May. They were taken for drives to the show places and soon began to agree with Mrs. Elton that Surrey must really be the 'garden of England', no matter the claims of other counties.

The congregation at the wedding consisted almost entirely of the family group—William and his wife, Lizzie and her husband, and Tony. The whole business seemed to be done by a turn of the wrist. Lizzie was rather shocked at Mary's having had to repress a laugh at one point in the proceedings, and reproved her for it afterwards. But Mary was not to be damped by anything. 'Nonsense, Lizzie dear, why shouldn't I be amused? It's far too serious to be solemn about.'

Tony's description of the simplicity and rate of the wedding ceremony amused Reskadinnick. 'Just like Mary, she does everything in a hurry,' was the comment. 'But I'm afraid she won't have a child in a hurry,' thought her father ruefully, 'she's thirty-eight. What a pity this didn't happen a few years ago.'

But that was where the wise old man miscalculated. She was married on June 2nd. Punctually on March 2nd, arrived a fine boy. No one could help laughing, least of all Mary herself. She considered it indelicate to mention the possibility beforehand, so the news came to Reskadinnick as a gorgeous surprise. All the servants, farm-hands, and cottagers within hail were summoned into the front kitchen to be told the joyful news—the first of a new generation, and a boy, and a fine one, and Miss Mary's. Drinks abounded.

Tony fled hot-foot for the North, and it was just as well, for Mary couldn't afford a good nurse to take the place of the harridan who was officiating for the time. The house, when Tony found it at last, was in a most unprepossessing street. It's very name—Lawton Road—struck a chill on her. 'Poor Mary,' she thought, 'after the spaciousness of Reskadinnick to be cooped up in a street!' A cheery little maid opened the door wide, and assured her in answer to quick inquiries, that all was well, and would she take off her things before going in to see the mistress.

A surprise awaited her. There was no more idea of 'poor

Mary'. The room struck a gay note. Some pale, spring sunshine was pushing in; a bright fire was airing tiny clothes; and Mary was holding up a warning finger lest Tony should wake up little Tom. In the background stood the harridan, a folio edition of the old-fashioned nurse, eyeing Tony with outward deference, but sourly. Mary had all the signs, well known to Tony, of suppressed laughter. As soon as the nurse had to go out of the room, she let her laughter loose.

'I've nearly burst my swathing-bands over that old nurse —Melpomene I call her—for she is so lugubrious that laughter is the only way to bear it. In the course of her genial chat after the doctor had left she said, "Folks mostly dies on the third day." Then she shook her head over baby, recounting case after case in which the baby had died. One demise was so sudden as to surprise even her. "Lor, mum, I stood putrified." '

In spite of Mary's protests that Melpomene was worth her weight in gold for sheer humour, Tony saw it otherwise, and determined to get rid of her at once.

'You and I between us will manage baby splendidly. If only your little servant can do a bit of cooking, washing, and cleaning, we shall be all right.'

'I'm perfectly well,' said Mary, 'and if it weren't for the look of the thing I could have got up the second day. And Susan will do anything for us. She has been so devoted to baby and me. She slipped in to encourage me when I was in the middle of things. "Soon be over, mum," says she; "think of what's coming." I asked her where the master was. "In the dining-room, mum, a-reading of the newspaper."

Then she added with a knowing look, "but he 's got it upside down." '

' How did she get on with Melpomene? '

'Disliked her to the full, was always afraid of her doing some injury to me or little Tom. "Her blew her breath on it," she complained to me one day, because she had seen Melpomene cooling my gruel *au naturel*.'

'A good little soul,' said Tony. 'I can trust her to look after you all.'

When Tony had to tear herself away from the jolly little family, to return to Cornwall, Mary carried on well enough, and as soon as the summer came and Tom could take a holiday, there were pressing demands for the three to come to Reskadinnick. Granny was craving to have the little grandson in her arms.

All went well on the journey until Truro. After that little Tom began to cry. Now Mary had discovered that on the very few occasions when he cried it was due to one of three causes: either he wanted food, or he wanted changing, or he was merely bored. Since she had fed him and just changed him, by the process of elimination she concluded that he was bored. So she pointed out to him the main features of the passing scenery; this failing, she held him upside down to look at the floor, then crooned to him, rocked him to and fro, got his father to take shifts at the exercise, and in short put him through all the natural shocks that baby flesh is heir to. But the howling grew steadily worse, reaching a frantic pitch during the hearty rocking that his father gave him. How thankful Mary was to see Tony at the front door eager to take charge.

'I can't think whatever is the matter with the child. For goodness' sake take him and get him quiet before mother has him. He has howled incessantly ever since I changed him at Truro.'

'Ah, then, perhaps that 's where the mischief was,' said Tony, and taking the baby quickly to pieces she exclaimed: 'Why you pinned a bit of little Tom himself into the machinery! The dear of him! The poor lamb! No wonder he screamed. It 's nothing to laugh at, Mary. There, there, my pet, you're all better now.' And so it was. A wide-eyed, smiling boy was placed in his grandmother's lap.

The following year another boy arrived. Mary refused to let Tony come to her, for Granny was getting too old to be left. But Fan was delighted to go to stay at Rainhill and do her best. Her best ended in her being very shortly married to a well-to-do cotton merchant of Liverpool, a friend of Tom's. Her presence or absence made little difference to Mary, who by now had developed a technique of her own for dealing with children: absolutely clean all over once a day; as much dirt as they liked during the day; regular food and habits; and for the rest—wholesome neglect.

Meanwhile Tom was doing fairly well, but soon found mining and everything to do with it a horribly uncertain business. 'You never know where you are with a mine,' Cap'n Vivian had warned him, 'I only stick to it because I can't bear to give up the old game.' Tom's ambition now was to be on the London Stock Exchange, where his knowledge of mining interests could be used to good account, as he explained to Mary.

'But the Stock Exchange is pretty uncertain, too, isn't it?' she objected.

'Yes, if you go in for gambling. But level-headed stockbrokers are badly needed, if only to keep the ordinary investor sane, by advising him, and avoiding such silly manias as we had on the railways.'

So the plan was to go to London and live as cheaply as possible. Tom reckoned that it would cost less if he lived out of town, so he went up by himself to see what he could find. He soon had a delightful surprise for Mary—a tiny cottage, actually within Epping Forest, with the romantic name of Little Monkhams. It was like something out of a fairy story—tiny rooms, a pretty little lawn in front, a honeysuckle-covered porch, where Mary sat to do her mending, and no neighbours to overlook. The two little boys, Tom and Vivian, were able to roll about to their hearts' content, and thrive. Their father went off to the City every morning by train, and the line passed close enough for Mary to take them to wave to him. After this she would dismiss the boys with her favourite command: 'absquatulate' (a word that William had brought her from his visit to America).

There must have been something infectious about Mary's matrimonial career, for the next piece of surprising news at Reskadinnick was the promise of another grandchild in the double menage in Surrey. After eleven years of married life, William's wife had settled down into complacent childlessness. It was a shock to her therefore when the doctor informed her of what was happening. Always ready to look on the gloomy side of life, she drew Lizzie's husband aside, and with a long face of dismay broke the news to him on his return from the City in these words: 'Isn't it dreadful! They say I'm in the family way!' Astounded out of all decorum he exclaimed, 'Good God, Frances, by whom?' The merriment in the home circle over this remark was mainly due to Frances having repeated it to them all with immense indignation.

Before the year was out Mary's third boy arrived. The Forest was not the handiest place in the world for such events, and as Mary considered it unnecessary to inform a doctor or engage a nurse beforehand, little Charles nearly died. Fortunately Lizzie was on a Christmas visit to them and saved the baby's life by some kind of natural instinct of which she had no recollection afterwards. Poor Lizzie would have given the world to have a child herself, and treasured the sayings and doings of the little crowd at Monkhams.

In the following spring, before Charles was three months old, there was a grand parade of the three boys in London. Mary insisted on taking them all up by train, to join in the celebrations for the wedding of the Prince of Wales. Their father looked after the two elder boys, Tom and Vivian, three and two, and Lizzie carried baby Charles. Mary superintended generally, feeling that she was showing Princess Alexandra what could be done in the way of boys. She bought three of the white satin favours that were being sold in the streets, and pinned one on each child, while their father bought three slices of wedding-cake for the grownups. Each slice was iced all over, and had a likeness of the Prince on one side and one of the Princess on the other.

The cake was duly eaten, but the favours, with the date March 10th, 1863, and the name of the child on each, were preserved as mementoes.

Also carefully preserved was little Tom's first effort at a letter, written in Cornwall and showing evidence (by its sudden jerks and yet good spelling) of his hand being guided by a grown-up: 'Tom will go to Godrevy. Mamma wants to go to Portreath but Tom likes the little waves at Godrevy best. Mamma may go to Portreath if she likes but Tom shall go to Godrevy first and Vivian wants to go to Godrevy first. Sammy shall drive Tom in the wagon.'

When in the following year Mary's fourth boy was announced Cap'n Vivian sent with his congratulations a demand to know when she was going to contrive a little maid, another Mary Vivian for him. To which she replied that she would do her best, but had little hope, for she seemed to run to boys. She added that if ever she were considered good enough to be blessed with a little girl, she would take enormous care that the poor child should not be so utterly spoilt as she herself had been.

EIGHT

OTTO

'It's all very well,' wrote Mary to her sister, 'to laugh at me for having my children so quickly, but there's a lot to be said for it. The little scamps keep one another company and educate one another. I discovered a tiny school here, and have been taking Tom to it every day. But no, it's really too absurd, he learns such rubbish, he does far better getting dirty in the garden. Take my advice, Tony, and have your children quickly. We've named baby "Barnholt", and Otto has not only consented to stand godfather, but has sent a lovely silver mug. The name should have been Otto, but we felt that Barnholt was so much more uncommon and distinguished. I think he will turn out like Otto, for he is fair and strong and full of adventure. 'Tis true he cannot walk yet, but he crawls most emphatic, and eggs on his brothers to mischief as well as his very small vocabulary permits. Hurry up, Tony, and let us see what you can do in this line.'

The old people had no longer any complaint to make of the lack of grandchildren, and the balance of sex was also adjusted. Not only had William's little girl Beatrice turned out to be very clever, but Joe too had married and had a daughter. And tin was going up. This metal acted as a kind of family barometer, its price being the almost daily excitement. It was impossible to keep Cap'n Vivian above ground for long. In a letter to Mary dated August 1864 he wrote:

Dearest child, your handsome little birthday present came to hand in due course and was received with as much pleasure and parental feeling as if it had been worth a hundred pounds. I hope the time is not far distant when we shall all have a little flood tide. I am very anxious to see you with Tom and the dear children; kiss them and bless them all for me.

When the horse fell with poor old Sammy and myself I had a very severe fall, but thank divine Providence I am got pretty well again. I went underground on Saturday last for the first time and got on very well. Our mines on the whole are looking a little more promising than for some time past, but thus far drawing away money rather too fast; however, in the midst of it all I might spare a trifle to a beloved child. Therefore if you find yourself short and are in want of a few little things you must leave [let] me know it with as much ease as you would ask for sixpence when you were about seven years old.

Beyond all other cause for rejoicing at Reskadinnick was the approaching marriage of Tony. The long time of waiting had come to an end, and the wedding was fixed for the coming spring. Old Mr. Barnholt had left everything in his will to Otto, to settle as he thought best. Accordingly he had made over the big house to his two sisters, never likely now to be married, and assured them a good income. Partly owing to the boom in railways the timber trade was doing well, and there was plenty for himself and Tony to live on in their new house.

This new house she had seen in its early stages, a dream

of a house, overlooking the fjord and the pine-clad hills beyond. Every letter from him gave some extra detail about it; a fine bay window had been added, where Tony could sit and sew or sketch or read, and wave to him as he went over to the saw-mills. There was mention, too, of a special little room into which the sun shone most of the day, the very thing for a playroom, 'where I hope my little godson from Epping Forest may come to play, and perchance show his *cousins* a thing or two.' So far, he said, he had bought very little furniture, only the sheer necessities, because he hoped that together they might pick up pieces they liked on their travels. His business would take him to many countries, and what fun they would have going about together, and dropping in at Reskadinnick or at Little Monkhams when they were least expected.

The idea was that he should come to fetch her at the end of April, and that they should be married on her birthday. The wedding was to be a quiet one at the little church of Penponds, although there were such rumours afloat of local enthusiasm that it was feared the church would be over-flowing before the bride arrived. 'Her'll have to squeeze in,' was the opinion on the downs.

'Have it all as quiet as you suggest, Tony darling,' wrote Otto, 'but I warn you that there will be nothing quiet about your reception here in Skien. The whole neighbourhood is figuring to itself to be *en fête*. They know you like songs and dances, and they intend to drown you in songs and dances. The men told me yesterday that they are making a triumphal arch. Even the children are getting flags ready.'

This was all very amusing, but Grannie's mind was more

occupied with the trousseau, and she was for ever counting over half a dozen of this and a dozen of that. It would never do for Norway to notice any falling short in this matter on the part of Cornwall. Fine sewing she could no longer do, but there was no lack of this from the numerous 'cousins' in Camborne. Gifts kept arriving of exquisitely embroidered handkerchiefs, scarves with lace-work so fine that Tony wondered how any eyes could have accomplished it, and bordered pillow-cases too good for any one but a visitor. The only fly in the ointment (mentioned in various ways in every letter accompanying a gift) was the loss of Tony herself, and what they would do without her they didn't know. Tony felt these expressions deeply, and most of all when they were painfully and ungrammatically written and enclosed in a parcel with some hideous little vase or woollen mat from the cottagers on the downs or their children. Mary wrote that it was a question between sending a present or coming down for the wedding—it wouldn't run to both —and she had decided to get away if only for the one day, because Tony couldn't be properly married without her.

After the long years of waiting, sheer bliss was Tony's at last, as Otto's letters kept arriving, full of excited anticipation of their happiness. She was ashamed to catch herself sometimes too happy, and not regretful enough at leaving everybody.

It was half-way through March, and the next letter from Otto would probably be to fix the date when he was intending to sail from Norway. But the post brought nothing that week. 'Too busy to write' was the general opinion, and when the next week went by without a letter it was con-

fidently concluded that he had already started and meant
to take them by surprise. 'He may put his head in at the
front-kitchen door any moment,' said Mrs. Vivian, 'and I
shall get his room ready.' But Tony knew Otto better, and
couldn't help being a bit anxious, for surely he could have
found time to scrawl a line. Another post went by a blank,
and Tony pretended to fall in with the accepted idea that
Otto was on his way. She threw herself vigorously into the
daily routine, to make the time pass until the next post.

Great was her relief therefore one morning to be told that
Captain Theiste was in the front-kitchen and asking to see her.

'Tell him I am coming,' said she, as she hastily dried her
hands. Thoughts raced through her head—Theodore had
brought a letter for her—perhaps Otto had been obliged to
go on some business trip that took longer than he thought
—or was he ill?

She found Theodore standing against the table, with his
back to the window. In response to her eager greeting he
began at once—

'Otto has sent me——'

'Yes, yes, with a letter and the latest news——'

'Well, yes, in a way. I've got no letter actually, but there
is news to tell you. Where are the others?'

'Oh, we won't wait for them. Father is down at the tin-
streams, and mother is really not up yet; I keep her in bed
as late as I can. Joe is probably gone to the mill, and may
not be in for an hour.'

'Good,' said Theodore, as he went to shut carefully both
the door into the kitchen and the one into the garden. 'The
fact is, I rather wanted to see you alone.'

'Alone?' said Tony, 'the news is not *bad*, Theodore?'

'Well, not of the best—You remember, don't you, the good ship *Skien*?'

'Of course I do, what a question!' said Tony, relieved beyond measure that the bad news had to do with the ship, and not with——

'Sit down, dear, because it's rather a long story about her,' and Theodore gently pushed Tony on to the settle and hitched himself up on to the table. 'That vessel was like a bit of Otto's own self, as it had been of his father's. When dear old Captain Christian retired, a new skipper had to be found——'

'And I expect he was a failure,' interrupted Tony.

'Not a bit of it; he was excellent. For over twenty-five years the *Skien* had plied to and fro across the North Sea and up and down the Channel, and never the slightest mishap—not the loss of a spar.'

'And now you are going to tell me that something has gone wrong with her,' said Tony, whose nerves were getting a little frayed by Theodore's deliberate manner.

'Yes, but listen. When the time came at the beginning of the year to pay the usual insurance money on her, Otto thought he would take a leaf out of Mary's book, and risk something. He told me that he had thought how very handy that insurance money would be just then to buy a good piano for the new house, for Tony to play on.'

'And so he let the insurance slide?'

'Yes. And I only wish to goodness that I had been there and prevented such a foolhardy idea.'

Tony's heart leapt with relief—so all this fuss was merely

about money. 'So he has had no compensation for the damage to the vessel? Oh, Theodore, you needn't make such a tale of woe about it. He'll soon make it up. One would think from your solemn manner that something really dreadful had happened.'

'Well, it was worse than a mere bit of *damage* to the *Skien*. She was lost with all hands.'

At this Tony's overwrought nerves gave way and she began to sob. Theodore fidgeted again at the doors, to see that no one was likely to disturb them, then went to the grocery cupboard in the corner.

'What are you looking for?' said Tony.

'I thought perhaps a drop of brandy might put you right.'

'What nonsense!' said Tony, brushing away her tears, 'I'm perfectly right. So foolish of me to give way like this. I am ashamed to say that my tears were sheer relief.'

'Relief?' queried Theodore.

'Yes, relief that Otto was not on board, as he might well have been. The fact is that the last week or two I have been getting horribly worried about him, trying not to show it and not to feel it. And now here am I so relieved from *that* worry that I'm not grieved enough about those poor men and their wives.'

'That's the dreadful part of it. That's what has—— That's where Otto——That's why——' Theodore stumbled on for words.

'You need not try to tell me how Otto feels about it. He knew every one of the men personally, and took such an interest in them. What a heart-breaking work it must have been for him to go round to their wives——'

'Heart-breaking—that is the right word. The financial loss wouldn't have worried him so much in itself, only that it left him unable to provide for the widows and children as generously as he would have liked. He had scraped every penny together for them. Now, Tony dear, you must be as brave as you can over this bit of news—he had to sell the new house he was just finishing for you.'

'Brave!' cried Tony, 'what do you take me for? Do you really think that Otto and I care where we live? Why, we shall be perfectly happy in one of those timber huts on the fjord. It will make us seem nearer to the men and their troubles.'

'That's just like you, Tony dear, but the selling of that house was a terrible blow to Otto. He had so set his heart on it for you. He couldn't bring himself to write and tell you about it, and begged me to come and break the news to you.'

'Well, I must say you are a grand hand at breaking news, Theo. You might well have burst it upon me a little sooner without upsetting me. After all, there are far worse troubles than this to be faced, aren't there?'

'I'm afraid so,' muttered Theodore.

'And here am I,' said Tony with a laugh, 'never thanking you for coming all this way to let me know, and never getting you a meal or anything after your journey.' And she rose and went towards the kitchen door.

'It's all right; don't go, I had a meal in Camborne just before coming down. I have to be off to Falmouth again immediately—as soon as I have had a few words with Joe.' He glanced nervously out of the window. 'Sit down again. I haven't quite finished—I had a very special message to you from Otto.' Here he began to pace up and down with his captain's stride, not looking at Tony, but continually glancing out of the window.

'Do let me have it—quickly,' said Tony, trying to keep her seat patiently. 'Never mind the exact words.'

'As soon as I was fixed up for this trip to Falmouth I went over to see him, feeling sure he would like to send you a message. "Message, yes," says he, "I haven't had the heart to write. Let her know about everything, about the sale of the house, and how hard up I am. Tell her all, and then ask her if she can possibly wait a little longer." "Don't be a fool, man," said I, "Tony would wait for you till domesday."'

Here Theodore cast another anxious glance out of the window and said he hoped they wouldn't be interrupted.

'No, no, no one will come just yet. Go on, you were quite right to say I could wait till domesday.'

'Well, he turned on me such a look of misery as I have never seen. "This going round among the widows of the seamen," said he, "has been killing work, and I'm not the man I was. I can't bear to offer her such a broken life." And then he broke down, Tony dear, and to see a man in tears——'

'What he needs is me—at once—to help with the widows and children and managing and everything. I'll go to him at once. I'll go back with you to Falmouth—now,' and she got up and fumbled for the door, as though to get on her outdoor things there and then.

'No, Tony, you can't go to him. One moment more, dear. Sit down again. A few days later, just as I was going on board, a letter was handed to me. It was from Sophie.'

'A further message?' cried Tony, 'for the love of heaven let me have it quick. Was Otto too ill to write it himself. Was Otto——?'

Theodore stopped his pacing to and fro, turned his back to her, and staring out of the window, said: 'The letter was to say that Otto was dead.'

When he turned round, she was standing, looking out at the great elm trees. 'Yes, Otto, I will wait for you till domesday,' said she, and quietly went back into the kitchen and took up the work she had been doing.

§ 2

The news of Otto's death practically killed Granny, for she faded away in the course of a few months. Holding Tony's hand as she was dying, she was understood to mutter her favourite phrase, 'What a mercy——.' But no one could imagine to what she was referring, unless it was her own helplessness; for that indeed had required Tony's full attention, and probably provided the activity that is the only support for a crushing sorrow.

As soon as Mary heard of Otto's death she prepared to go down to Cornwall by the first train she could. Her impulse was to take baby Barnholt and put him in Tony's lap. But Tom, always the most deliberate of men, had a wiser instinct in the matter, and thought that such an action might be more terrible than anything else at the moment. 'Just go alone,' said he, 'she will want *you*.'

'There's nothing to be said,' thought Mary on her

melancholy journey down. 'What can I *do* for Tony?'
And she resolved that her four boys should belong as much
to Tony as to herself; there would be no need to teach them
to love and respect her—no one could help that—but she
should *have* them in that peculiar way that only a woman
understands. She kept that resolve. Few things are more
remarkable in the remarkable friendship of the two sisters
than the whole-hearted way in which the children loved
Tony. In the following year the long-desired daughter
entered the list, another Mary Vivian (called Molly to dis-
tinguish her from her mother). Tony made no attempt to
capture the love of these children by special expressions of
affection or by spoiling. Mary must have been aware that
they adored their aunt, but never a ghost of jealousy
appeared; indeed they could never be enthusiastic enough
about Tony to please Mary. Children are surely quick to
feel the darkness of jealousy before they are old enough to
give it a name. With Mary there was no taint of it; the sun
of Cornwall had drawn all such humours from her; and she
saw to it that her children should not fall victims to it. For
fun they used to ask her sometimes which of them she
loved best. Her answer never varied: 'The one that first
gives me a silk dress.' Since her care for dress was ludicrously
non-existent, she could hardly have hit on a better rebuff.

It was mainly in the summer holidays that Tony had
Mary's children trooping round her. But before long she
had the opportunity of dealing with children all the year. Bad
news came from Surrey. Instead of paying attention to his
father's warning, William had allowed Lizzie's husband to
share his banking account, with the result that the latter

had been drawing cheques just as he felt disposed. He had
been cunningly careful for a long time, but William's complete
lack of suspicion tempted him to go the pace, and at last
he decamped with what he could. Ostensibly he went on a
visit to London, taking Lizzie with him to give colour to the
idea. Never was he known to show her any affection, or
desire for her company. As soon as she discovered what he
had been doing, her conscience forbade her to go on living
on the proceeds. Her duty to him, always a forced one,
seemed to be at an end, and she left him. With a little help
from her father and from Tom and Mary she managed to
make a living by teaching music. She would have been happy
enough in her quiet way if her husband had left her alone.
But time after time he would find out where she was living
and pursue her. She changed her lodgings continually in
order to elude him, but he would always discover them, no
one knew how, and get money out of her. He would put up
a tale of a reformed life and total abstinence and even pretend
affection, but he would steal her belongings to sell them for
drink, sometimes even her clothes. On one occasion he
hawked some pieces of her furniture on a barrow down the
street where she was living. Now and again Mary took her
little girl on a visit to Lizzie, and even the small child felt
the atmosphere of discomfort and anxiety. Lizzie seemed to
have one eye on the gate all the time. One dreadful day he
actually arrived while they were there. His ugliness was so
repulsive that it almost frightened Molly. No wonder he
had no friends. Tom used to say that his reason for drinking
was always the fifth rather than the second.

Providence appeared to awake to its business at last. He

met his death in the street, probably through drunken lack of control, for he was never quite sober. Mary and Tony didn't bother to inquire into the details, for they were only too glad at Lizzie's release. According to rigorous Victorian custom his widow wore the deep mourning prescribed. But never were these dreadful trappings more misplaced, for really she was delivered from a nightmare. In her case a sense of duty killed not only a sense of humour but even a sense of tragedy. Tony would have respected her more if she had run a stiletto into that unspeakable husband. Or is the deepest tragedy the incapacity for it? the unawareness of it? to be numbed by its misery instead of being exalted by its fury? If this be so, then Lizzie was the saddest figure of a family *haud ignara mali.*

To return to the immediate catastrophe of William's financial trouble. His business as a mine-broker was ruined, and he was unable to keep up his large house and maintain his wife and two children. Needless to say, they were all invited to Reskadinnick, to stay until his affairs were straight. That visit never came to an end. Cap'n Vivian put William to the management of certain of his mines, and Frances helped Tony in carrying on the work of the house. After a while a third child was born, and certainly Tony had enough to distract her mind from her own troubles. The new family settled down and took up their places in the old house for good. But Cap'n Vivian took care to make it perfectly clear that they were only guests, that the farm was to be always Joe's, and the house to be always Tony's. Each had worked unremittingly and deserved the results.

Tony therefore was absolute mistress of the grand old

place, and gloried in its beauties and its capacity for hospitality. Since she had faced the worst that life could possibly bring, her serenity was never perturbed. She stilled her craving for Otto with the lines 'Fear no more the heat of the sun'. The children around her kept her perpetually young. In addition to William's three, Joe's six girls and boys were continually running in, always sure of a warm welcome. But it was Mary's batch that she loved best.

The children too from the cottages scattered over the downs used to come far oftener than seemed necessary, for a 'happorth of scald milk', or a 'pennorth of apples'. Tony certainly gave them far more than their money's worth, but it was something else that drew them. She was never silly about any child, often indeed quite fierce in her manner, but she fascinated them by talking to them as if they were her equals in age, wisdom, and social position; also by her intimate knowledge of their concerns, however childish, as well as of their fathers' work and their mothers' ailments. For instance one day she met in the lane a ragged little boy of about four years old. She towered over him: 'What is this dreadful thing, Willie, that I hear—that you are in the habit of swearing?'

'Oh, no, Miss Tony,' came the bright reply, 'I don't now. I've given that up.'

As for the old and feeble people within her reach, goodness knows how many she went to see, and to subsidize in one way or another. She did it so quietly that it was only by side winds that any one ever knew about this part of her activity. 'Been out, Tony? Where have you been?' 'Just for a blow on the downs, up Gethan way—glorious sunset.'

Money she seemed to have no interest in at all, except to use it economically for the house or to give it away. She would probably have been penniless, but that she received a small annuity every May-day. Otto's words to his sisters as he was dying were an urgent wish that they should be good to Tony. They had planned how best to do this and managed to raise enough to buy this annuity for her. When tin was 'up' she was often quite wealthy from Cornish sources, but most of the money would filter away. The Norwegian money was a grand stand-by in the midst of the caprices of tin.

Drawing and painting she never touched again, but pushed forth all her intense interest in them into encouraging the children's attempts. Mary's third boy, Charles, showed a marked ability in this line, and it was mainly due to Tony's insistent demands to see what he had done that led him on to higher flights. Among her treasured possessions there was a letter from him when a boy of seventeen, consisting of seven pages, illustrated with as many pen-and-ink sketches, miniatures of the large water-colours he had done during a holiday in Cornwall, at the Lizard, Penzance, and so on. She had seen these when he had done them, but the letter was written to tell her what criticisms his master at school had passed on them—the light wrong here, the foreground poor there, the distance good in one, the trees in another. An aunt who could call forth such a letter from a boy filled a place that no mere mother could fill.

Mary's little girl lacked her brother's ability, but she was always making something 'for Tony'. Among her childish concoctions was a packet of illustrated visiting-cards. Of these the one that tickled Tony most was a picture of Venus

in a shell, with 'Miss Vivian' printed in old English letter-
ing beneath. Molly also made for her aunt an 'Atlas for
Beginners', consisting of many coloured maps, sewn together
and bound in cardboard, profusely supplied with lines of
latitude and longitude, feathery mountains and wriggly
rivers.

The most astounding thing about Tony, considering her
long years of waiting and the crushing end of her hopes,
was the atmosphere of enjoyment that always surrounded
her. Angry she certainly could be, but was never known
to be dismal. 'Ich habe genossen das irdische Glück; ich
habe geliebt und gelebet'—that must have been at the back
of her mind.

Her humour and light-heartedness were thrown into
strong relief by contrast with William's wife. The only
glamorous thing about the latter was her name—Frances
Knight Vivian—so aristocratic as compared with Tony's
plain 'Annie Vivian'. She was always called Aunt Frances,
but the children would have liked to call her Aunt Knight.
She was very religious and always kind, but took such a
miserable view of life that she seemed to be persistently
shaking her head over something and to be extremely aged.
The children never told her of their doings, being certain
that she would tell them not to do it again. Her daughter
Beatrice often damped any proposed adventure with the
words: 'Ma wouldn't like it.' Consequently the boys took
care that Ma should not be troubled by knowledge of it.

What chiefly annoyed Mary, when they were staying at
Reskadinnick, was the difficulty in getting Tony to join
them in some day's outing. Frances, having no personal

spirits for the jaunt, would say, 'No, I won't go to-day. But you all go off and enjoy yourselves. Don't mind me.' The consequence naturally was that Tony pretended that she couldn't go either, and stayed at home to keep Frances company.

It is difficult to see what was at the bottom of Frances' lugubrious view of life. Unlike Tony, she had a devoted husband, three children, and practically no household cares. But an unseemly incident that occurred at the death of Cap'n Vivian throws some light on it. No doubt she had been secretly galled for many years by the fact that 'Miss Vivian' was mistress of the house, while she, 'Mrs. Vivian', and wife of the eldest son, was in a subordinate position. Apparently she never considered that Tony had the care of the whole place on her hands, and had been deprived of all that a woman holds most dear.

Cap'n Vivian died as he had lived, in placid good humour. He had found it difficult to move about, so Tony put a little bell within reach for him to ring if he wanted anything. Hearing it one day while she was busy in the kitchen she ran as usual to his side, and found him dead. It was like the break-up of everything, not only to Tony but to the neighbourhood. Mary could not manage to leave home to come down to the funeral, but sent her eldest boy, Tom, then a young man of nearly eighteen. One hardly likes to inquire into the mind of Frances on that unhappy day. This is what Tom saw: the table was laid for tea immediately after the funeral, and there were several guests. Frances swept to the head of the table (which had been Tony's place ever since her mother's death) and proceeded to do the honours.

Tony must have been surprised, but she said nothing, and ever afterwards took a seat at the side. Tom of course was boiling with indignation, and Mary, when she heard about it, wrote a letter to Tony, wildly outspoken on the point. Tony's reply was characteristic: 'Nonsense dear,' she wrote, 'as if I cared where I sit! I am mistress of everything here, not because I sit at the head of the table, but because I do the work, and they can't get on without me. I often say to myself (in no Christian spirit, mind you), whosoever will be chief among you, let him be your servant. Poor Frances may as well have what pleasure she can get from sitting at the head of the table. Her pleasures are extremely few.'

NINE

CHARLIE

§ 1

EPPING FOREST was a curious place for Tom to choose
to live in. Cheap no doubt the cottage was, but its chief
attraction was its nearness to Buckhurst Hill, where there
was a station on the railway to town, and also, far more
important, a cricket club and ground. The game was a
passion with him, and the majority of his many friends came
to him in this connexion. Mary enjoyed their visits, exercis-
ing her ideal of hospitality upon them—to make no fuss
and to give them the best she had in the house. It was the
no fuss that was the main thing, for they knew that odd
hours, the smell of tobacco, or muddy boots left her quite
unperturbed. She even picked up some of the terms and
chief points about cricket.

Among these friends one was the prime favourite with
all the family—Tom, Mary, and the children alike. This
was a giant of a fellow with a black beard, always known
as Charlie-Absolom (like that, all in one breath). His
people were a wealthy family living in a large country villa
near by, at Snaresbrook. He was a Cambridge man, and it
was an amusing speculation as to how he had managed to
get through his Little-go, for he seemed to know nothing
well except cricket. Mary's third boy had been named after
him, and he had the status of a favourite uncle. He was
continually dropping in at Monkhams.

Towards the end of the sixties this beloved little cottage had to be given up. Times were bad, and Tom could no longer afford the railway fare. So he migrated to a tiny house in one of those inner suburban roads whose grandeur of name is in inverse proportion to their grandeur of nature. This one was called Queen Margaret's Grove, suggestive of a stately avenue of orange trees. One of the elder boys used to say in later years that the mere words 'Queen Margaret's Grove' would reduce him to profound misery—although he could recall no detail of the life there—a curious instance of a feeling being brought to memory entirely apart from the circumstances that occasioned it. The little girl's earliest recollection in life was of this period—her own christening. It chanced by sheer coincidence that the second boy had been christened on the same date as the first. Mary, regarding this as a lucky omen, determined that any future children should be christened on this date. Charles followed the rule respectably early, but Barnholt and Molly had to be put off year after year because the date was awkward. Hence it came about that at the ages of five and three these two *walked* up to the font of St. Jude's, Mildmay Park. Molly was seized with fright, for it was the first time she had been in the public eye; the place seemed full of people; she was far from her base; suddenly she turned and ran back to comforting arms in the pew, where she cried lustily. She wondered in later years whether she had ever been effectively regenerated, for she fancied the parson must have decided to call it a christening at a premature stage.

In 1870 Tom's fortune took a good turn and he came home one evening with the news that they could take the best house to be found to let in the neighbourhood. The very next day little Tom came running home to say that the top house of Canonbury Park was to let, and that it was grander than any other in the road, because it had a big white porch and a pathway of coloured tiles leading from the gate to the front steps. Big Tom wasted no time, but took it at once.

Then there was room to breathe, and room to put up a visitor. So Charlie-Absolom not only dropped in constantly as before, but frequently stayed a few days. There was enough room too for a restricted kind of cricket in the back garden, where a 'boundary' was over the wall into the road. Charlie was so pleased with this simple game that the children did not realize what an important man he was in the cricketing world. He played for Cambridge, for the Gentlemen, and for Kent. He had the reputation of being good all round, at batting, bowling, and fielding, rather than specially brilliant in any one of these. Consequently he was a tower of strength when things were going badly, for he could throw himself into any breach, and was always at his best when hope for his side was lowest.

He was chosen by Lord Harris to go with the team to Australia, to play for England, and was recorded as having 'scored a great personal triumph in the match at Melbourne'. A letter from the Oriental Hotel in Melbourne caused no little excitement to the family in Canonbury and was carefully preserved. It ran thus:

DEAR TOM,

Just a line to assure you of my safety in this ghastly country. We had rare fun coming out—very nice people on board, plenty of susceptible young ladies and a skipper who let us do just as we liked. We played cricket in fine weather, of which there was precious little, but we had capital practice fielding on deck by standing round the card players, for as soon as a card was played or a trick put down they were blown about in all directions; sometimes a whole pack would fly into the air and toward the sea, and then it was difficult to save the lot. At first a good many packs were spoiled, but we improved so that for the last three weeks not a single card was missed. We shall win, I think, all our matches here, at any rate from what I have seen as yet. Our life is a monotonous round of gaiety and dissipation, and I'm blowed if some of the girls won't marry a fellow whether he will or not, unless, like your humble servant, of adamantine nature; they are youthful Mrs. Mc-Stingers. The behaviour of the Indian contingent of passengers on the P. and O. steamer would prohibit that company from obtaining a dancing licence if it were necessary to apply to the Middlesex magistrates—they could not consistently with their recent decision grant it.

I have not yet killed a kangaroo (not even in a single letter, so I'm improving) but I'm rather a nailer with the boomerang; I am always allowed a field to myself when practising; I think this a polite compliment—however many people are in it the moment I begin to throw they seek the adjoining pastures and leave me to myself.

I shall not have time to write to John Moysey this mail, so remember me kindly to him, assuring him all his tales concerning the different ports 'en route' were awful lies, and his advice would have been fatal to any one trying it.

I hope you, wife, and family are all well; give my kind

regards to your wife, and please remember me to Daniel, wife, &c., and all other friends too numerous to enumerate. I shall be right glad to get back again. I have a schoolboy's list of days until we return, and religiously strike off one every morning—it's my one ray of sunshine.

It's summer here and 7 in the morning. It's winter with you and 10.15 in the evening; ain't it rum.

Your sincere friend
C. A. ABSOLOM.

This letter has all the air of Charlie's endeavour to belittle his pleasure in the tour, so as not to make Tom envious. With all Tom's love of the game he was not rich enough to give as much time to it as Charlie could, and he was not a brilliant player. But he did his best, and backed up by Mary's delight in being hospitable, and his own love of fun, he became the kind of centre of his own cricketing world. When well off, as he was more often than not as time went on, he was lavish in making the accompaniments of a match go off well; and when he was in low water he was just as welcome for his joviality. It was not that he made jokes or sang or had stories to tell, but rather from a peculiar power of thoroughly enjoying himself, and causing the others to enjoy themselves, whatever the weather or the contretemps.

Among Mary's treasures was the manuscript of a song, consisting of eight stanzas, written by a member of the Woodford Wells Cricket Club, to celebrate the first match of the season, and headed 'Written for that Prince of good fellows Tom Thomas'. Each stanza celebrated some special act of prowess. It opened with a tribute to Charlie:

As in the game so in the song we'll keep the ball a'rolling,
By calling your attention first to Absolom's fine bowling.

The poet was evidently gravelled to find anything excellent in Tom's play, so he wove in Tom's little witticism about himself thus:

There's a little fact to which your notice I must call now:
'Tis "I, Tom Thomas, made the greatest average of you all
now".

The two friends made a funny contrast, for while Tom was short and fair, Charlie was dark and colossal in all directions. Charlie, too, provided entertainment in the pavilion with a never-failing fund of good stories. From sheer affection every team in which he played called him the Boss. At one time he had been known as the 'Cambridge navvy', owing partly to his physique and partly to his complete disregard of the proper thing in the matter of clothes. In his very first match at Lord's he caused a sensation by playing in a red shirt and wearing no cap.

Legends grew up round him, exaggerated no doubt, but it would be a poor legend that wasn't. The one fact that every one remembered about him was his never having been seen with any kind of head-gear whatever the weather; on one occasion he saved a match on a grilling day by sticking at it when most of his side had collapsed with the heat. He would carry his own cricket bag for miles when a conveyance was lacking. A story ran of his once having caught a ball on the back of his hand at short slip. He

appeared never to be encumbered with any but the barest
necessities of life, thus enjoying Mary's ideal of a rich man.
Sometimes no doubt he found himself in a.hole in this way.
One of his yarns of such a hole described how he once let
himself out to a farmer as haymaker for the wage of five
shillings a day and his beer, and how at the end of the
second day the farmer implored him with tears in his eyes
to accept ten shillings a day and find his own beer.

His chief charm to Mary lay in his unconventionality
and his habit of coming out strong when things were going
badly. And he would help out any cricket team anywhere
that was in an emergency. For such a purpose Tom took
him down to stay at Reskadinnick one summer for a few
days, in order to play in a match for Camborne. There his
high delivery bowling and his eccentric hitting made hay
of the enemy—Redruth—much to the satisfaction of Camborne, for there exists an age-long rivalry between the two
towns.

Of course Tom's children gloried in all Charlie's feats and
in his frequent visits. They liked to see him perform miracles
with his enormous hands. He could balance a salt-cellar on
the back of his hand, throw it up so that it turned completely
over and then catch it again without spilling the salt. They
had a chair that was always called 'Charlie-Absolom's chair',
because he once sat in it. It was a low-seated, fancy cane
chair, always kept in the window facing the path up to the
front door, Mary's favourite coign of vantage. Charlie's
one occupation of it had left it 'never the chair it had been',
but had imparted to it a kind of heroic quality for having
retained its four legs.

During the winter months, when cricket was off, he would come quite as often, for long country walks with Tom and the boys, and for spinning yarns or playing whist in the evening. To Molly, as the youngest and a girl, he was a devoted slave. He would hoist her to the perilous height of his shoulder, and allow her to order him to various stations on the route to Cornwall, pretending to be *The Lord of the Isles* pulling up and starting with enormous puffings and blowings. Sometimes he would set her on his knees very gently and amuse her with a 'pretty tale' or with some part of his waistcoat, and then, suddenly, while she was absorbed, he would spread out his knees, and plop she would go to the floor. It was a fearful joy, for though she knew what was coming, she didn't know when. For this drama she would clamour encores until higher authority said 'enough'.

'Look here, Charlie,' said Mary to him, 'you'll have to be careful of your language in front of little Molly.'

'Oh, rather. I am aware of that. The other day I was telling the boys a funny thing had happened—a man had a tooth broken by a ball, and she pulled me up with "not sunny but pecoola".'

'Ah yes, but it's your strong language that she is picking up.'

'Whatever has she been saying?'

'The other morning she was observed standing in front of the fireplace, feet apart, hands behind her back and saying to herself, "I'm b'owed if there isn't a sire".'

'Well, I'm blowed!' laughed Charlie.

However, her expression on another occasion could not be laid at his door. The family were having a holiday at

Walton-on-the-Naze, and had joined forces with an uncle and his wife. The husbands came down for the week-ends, often by steamer. On this particular day Mary and her sister-in-law took little Molly with them on to the pier to meet Tom and his brother Alfred. Behold, much to the child's satisfaction, Charlie-Absolom turned up with them. After hearty greetings Tom started off along the pier with Mary on his arm, followed by Alfred and his wife. There was Charlie, left standing alone, a little out of it, Molly felt. So, stepping up to his side and reaching for his arm she said, 'I'm not your wife, but I will be your concubine.' It had been explained to her in reading about Solomon that this was a kind of second-rate wife; and she was greatly puzzled at the burst of laughter that greeted her reference to something out of the Bible.

§ 2

Mary had a genuine horror of match-making, but she could hardly bear to see such a fine fellow as Charlie being wasted, and asked him one day, 'How is it you have never married? I should love to see you with some riotous boys of your own, and teaching them how to bat.'

'It isn't that I haven't considered it, but the only woman who really——' he broke off and added hurriedly, 'I'm hard to please. I daren't risk getting tied to a fusser—or a nagger—or a whiner—or, worst of all, an adorer.'

Mary laughed at each specimen as he slowly named it, able on her part to supply mentally an illustration from her own circle.

'Now if,' went on Charlie, 'you could find me some one

of the same kind as yourself I would do my utmost to induce
her to put up with my ways, and perhaps we could contrive
as jolly a little family as you and Tom have managed—but
there isn't any such woman.'

'How about Tony?'

Charlie shook his head, 'No good, no good—Look here,
I'll tell you something. You remember that time two seasons
back when Tom and I were staying down there? When we
had that match with Redruth (and beat 'em by Jove). Well,
I saw enough of your sister then to know that there was no
woman on earth to come near her—not even you.'

'That's right—it's nuts and figs to me to hear any one
praising her like that—go on.'

'I know you are cleverer and handsomer and all that, but
Tony just bowled me out first ball.'

'Yes, and I know what you are going to say next—that
she was charmingly friendly up to a point.'

'Exactly. At the crucial point she turned on me almost
furiously. . . . I can't understand it.'

'I knew she would refuse you, because this kind of thing
has happened again and again. As you may suppose she
has had innumerable offers, and has turned them all off.
But I am struck with your saying that she was furious—it's
hopeful.'

'What do you mean, hopeful?'

'Tony is peculiar in this way, that if she doesn't care very
much she is polite and kind in her manner, but always when
her feelings are stirred unhappily she snaps out in a fit of
temper. She was probably greatly attracted by you, and
could only push you off by this outburst.'

'But why push me off?'

'Well, the only way in which I can make you really understand is to tell you her story. She never speaks of it herself, nor do any of us. But I want you to know it.'

Mary told him of the first visit to Norway, of Otto's love, of the long waiting, the meeting in London, the visits to Cornwall, the last happy visit of Tony to Norway, the building of the new house, the preparations for the wedding. She had never detailed it all out before, and when she came to the breaking of the news of Otto's death tears sprang to her eyes as the cruelty of Tony's fate struck her afresh. Charlie had sat motionless through her recital, but at this point broke in quietly.

'What was the actual cause of his death?'

'They say there is no such thing as a broken heart, but this was as near it as anything can be. I suppose it was a kind of nervous breakdown, to judge by his sisters' letters.'

'And this man, Theodore Theiste, I wonder he didn't feel strongly drawn to Tony himself.'

'No doubt he did, but he was more like a brother to her, and anyhow a woman would never be drawn to a man something *like* her lover, would she?'

To this Charlie grunted acquiescence, and Mary went on, 'I suppose that feeling is at the root of the objection to marrying a deceased wife's sister. Theodore was sufficiently like Otto—in physique and nationality and so on—to be a continual reminder of the man she had lost.'

'Yes, I see what you mean, but I don't see where any hope for me comes in.'

'Why partly in your extreme contrast in appearance, in

pursuits and tastes. And yet, underneath such exteriors you are just the kind of man she has always admired—big and strong and determined.'

'Yes, but this Otto appears from what you say to have been a man of culture—literary and all that. And you know the rough sort of fellow I am.'

'Listen, Charlie, don't be a fool about this literary business. I suppose I oughtn't to sing my sister's praises, but honestly she is the most intellectual person I have ever come across. With her it's not the result of learning but an attitude to life. She is so alert and sympathetic with all kinds of interests. Why she would get as much poetry out of a game of cricket as out of a play of Shakespeare's.'

'What a woman!' broke in Charlie.

'And then she loves unconventional people, and cares not a rap for fine clothes or comforts. "Life is a battle" is her favourite saying. And so indeed it has proved for her. How I long for her to have a bit of freedom and happiness —such as you could give her.'

'But I've knocked about a lot, you know, have led a devil-may-care sort of life.'

'Yes, but, Charlie, you are real. She once said to me that she preferred Charles II to Charles I because she liked even a bad man who was decided and knew his mind—far preferable she contended to a good man on whom one could never rely. You see what I mean? Strength, that's what appeals to her.'

'Lord! What a companion she would be for a bit of adventure!'

'Yes, she would be game to go anywhere with you and

charge a rhinoceros if necessary. I remember once, years ago, her telling me how she was left alone in the house. Every single soul was out in the harvest-field, for the usual rush, and she was busy getting food ready for their return. Two tramps appeared at the kitchen door and demanded beer. "There's nothing for you," said she, "until you've done some work in the harvest-field—go along." At this they walked into the kitchen and said they meant to have beer and some of her pasties. Quite quickly she stepped over to the recess where the wood is chopped, seized the chopper, brandished it, and said, "Clear out at once".'

'Oh, don't tell me any more about her. It will only make a second refusal harder to stand.'

'But when she put you off it was when you knew nothing of her story. I believe that if you let her know that I have told you all about it—that if you talk freely of Otto— boldly and sensibly as you naturally would, Charlie, she may see things in a new light.'

'The poor fellow himself would be the first to wish that she shouldn't sacrifice her life for him—if he was the sort of man you describe.'

'Exactly. We have all felt that. But none of us somehow have ever been able to mention the idea to her, to mention Otto's name even. You know how it is in a family. Never comes the occasion. One is so afraid of opening old wounds and leaving them open when there's no getting away from it. It has been like that in my own case. But you, coming in from a distance, having heard the story freshly, can——'

'Yes, I see, and I'll have a try.' So saying, Charlie got up and without another word strode out.

Some time passed before Mary heard any more, and she had come to the conclusion that the second attempt had been a failure, since her letters from Tony had made no mention of it, nor even anything but the most casual reference to Charlie's visit. However, a letter arrived from him at last, with no address and a postmark she couldn't decipher.

'You were right,' he wrote, 'in almost every particular. It was quite plainly a relief to her to speak about Otto to some one who knew what she had gone through and what he was like. In fact she told me a good deal more about their love story than even you know—things she had never told any one before. She has been bottling up her grief too much—I could see that. She admitted freely that Otto would wish her to have a husband and home and happy life. She even admitted that she loved me. And this I know was true, a man is never mistaken about that. But the idea of marrying any one but Otto is simply unthinkable to her. When I boldly put it to her, she didn't blow my head off, she . . . well never mind what she did. But I think a blow might have been easier to bear.'

§ 3

In the height of cricket fever, when the deeds of W. G. Grace were the talk of England, Charlie-Absolom vanished. It was not until ten years later that Mary's eldest boy, Tom, saw a notice of his death in the paper, with an appreciation of him by Lord Harris. The news came from Trinidad, reported in the *Port of Spain Gazette*, and stated that Mr.

Absolom was a purser on board the steamer *Muriel*, which was discharging a cargo of sugar on a Saturday evening. There was need for haste, and Mr. Absolom lent a hand to the work. A derrick fell on him, injuring him in such a way that he could not be moved into the hospital for many hours. He lingered on in intense pain, but fully conscious, until he died on the Monday afternoon.

He was only forty-three. Where had he been after leaving England in the seventies? Why was he a purser? His old friends' grief for him was mingled with these enigmas. And they would never have known, had it not been for a casual reference to him when Molly was writing to a friend of later days. This drew forth the following story:

'Charlie-Absolom! Now listen. When you were a girl of about twenty, I joined my regiment at Prospect Camp, Bermuda, a little hill-top, terraced for barracks (wooden huts made for the Crimea), a parade ground, and a small cricket field. The site is well named, for it must have one of the fairest prospects on earth—of other still smaller hills clothed with palms and cedar trees, and decked with flowering shrubs. Between these hill-tops and beyond, a hundred tiny coral islands set in pure cobalt specked with tiny white sails.

'Soon after I joined, the Regiment XI were challenged to play a cricket match with the Hamilton Town C.C. The date must be next Saturday, and the time 2 o'clock; no other day or earlier hour would suit. On Saturday morning, however, they cancelled the match, for no good reason, but said they would play on Saturday a fortnight later. This time Hamilton turned up ready for the fray—the usual unimpressive lot, which had been well beaten two or three times before.

'There was, however, one new-comer in the side, who, in that galley, looked noticeably out of his natural surroundings. A stiffly-built, weather-beaten man, wearing rather rough clothes, an air of rugged independence and self-confidence, but no hat.

'I recollect a look of power in his eyes, and seem to remember a scar on face or arm. To me, at nineteen, he seemed to be of extreme antiquity—and—he had a black beard.

'He was Mr. Smith, or Brown, or Jones. . . .

'The Regiment team was a fairly good one, and included C. W. Bengough, former captain of Rugby and Sandhurst, said by good judges to be the best bowler in England; also H. B. Hawke, whose brother was captain of Yorkshire for many years.

'Hamilton won the toss, and sent in old "Mr. Smith" first with another man. To the quick eye of youth his movements were stiff and slow, but his eyes were quick enough, watching the ball right on to the bat. Soon his strong arms started hitting the ball, hitting it hard, often, and all over the place. He made about 50, and the other ten of his side less than that altogether.

'Then the Regiment went in, and hanged if stiff old "Smith" didn't open the bowling. His shoulder didn't function freely to start with, and I think his first few balls were "outers". Then he got going, and so did we—out. In quick time he got wicket after wicket. The Regiment was out for a trivial score and well beaten. It was "Smith's" match.

'It then transpired that "Smith" was purser of the mail-boat which had arrived that morning from New York, and came every alternate Saturday. He was to have come the previous trip, but something prevented.

'That was his last game of cricket, and he never came to Bermuda again. He changed, as purser, into a ship running from New York to the West Indies, and on his very first trip to the Caribbean there was an accident. A derrick broke, fell on him and killed him.

'Did you know that that was the end of the friend of your childhood, Charlie-Absolom, who used to bowl you lobs, and who was in his time one of the finest cricketers alive?

'Not long after I read an article about him in an English paper, which was to this effect: Suddenly, in the hey-day of his cricket career, without known cause, he had left England for America, and cricket knew him no more. He lived, not in New York, but in the Rocky Mountains, with a tribe of Red Indians, who called him by some weird name, meaning "the man who never wears a hat".

'How long he was with the Red Indians I have no idea, but in course of time some white wanderer in the Rockies got news that another white man was lying, seriously injured by a bad fall, with a certain tribe, who were looking after him. So he sought, and found, Absolom, and somehow managed to get him to a town, and into hospital. There in due course he was patched up, but on being discharged was told by the doctor that it was essential he should go on a sea-voyage.

'Remembering the cricket match at Prospect, I conclude

that his method of getting a sea-voyage was to secure a job as purser on the Bermuda mail-boat.

'Only once was he known to have returned to England. He was, I believe, a member of the M.C.C. Committee, and one day, there was Absolom, sitting in his place at Lord's. Then again, and for the last time, he vanished.'

TEN

TOM

§ 1

WHAT was it that drove Charlie to England again for that brief visit? A longing to see another game of first-class cricket? An overwhelming fit of home-sickness? Certainly it was not his own numerous and scattered family that drew him. He had seldom been observed in their midst. No doubt it was just the old country. Whatever the main pull may have been, he is certain to have made straight for the cheery home in Canonbury, where everything was bound to be just the same as ever, and where he was dead sure of a rapturous welcome from Tom and Mary and all the youngsters. During the voyage over he would be thinking up all the adventures he had to tell, how Mary would enjoy his account of the dire straits he had been in, how the boys would egg him on to tell them of his narrow escapes from man and beast, and above all how Tom would revel in the more select stories intended for his ear alone. The thought would come that he had been away for years, and changes of some kind there were sure to be. Tom would be mellowed a bit—a better man of humour than ever. Mary could be counted on to be the same care-free purveyor of hospitality and *bonhomie*. Would the boys be too grown-up for a game of cricket in that old back garden? Would little Molly be too big to be kissed? Anyhow, ten to one Mary would be sitting in the window, in 'Charlie-Absolom's chair'.

His visit to Canonbury can be easily imagined. For desolation there is little to equal that of a returning exile confronted with an empty house where he had confidently looked for a welcome. An empty house, however, can look pathetic, can join in the exile's loneliness, and seem almost to be listening with him for the sound of the old footsteps and voices. A deadlier chill awaits the finding of the same old house occupied by strangers. The approaches to the house one can imagine full of pleasant anticipation. Charlie must have enjoyed the familiarity of the old suburban railway and the walk up the unchanged road—all that flavour of a neighbourhood that nothing short of an earthquake or a town-planning scheme can destroy. And as he drew near the house he would see the coloured tessellated pavement and the gate whose joke he knew well (the 'contrivance' for opening it was to hurl yourself against it). But what were all these white curtains? Had Mary grown proper? To complete his misgiving it needed only the ignorance of the servant as to the former tenants and her polite indifference as to their concerns.

That trip to England was probably Charlie's first sea-voyage in accordance with the doctor's orders. Evidently something or other that was disappointing or uncongenial in England sent him back immediately to the West Indies, where he took on work as a purser. It is fairly certain that if he had been able to trace the whereabouts of his old friends of Canonbury he would have done so. And if he had had the faintest rumour of their unhappy story, he would have sought them out. There is too the possibility that he felt after his long absence that sense of being forgotten and 'out of it' wherever he turned in England, and that that in itself was sufficient to send him back to a simpler kind of life. One thing can definitely be predicated of him—that wherever he happened to be he was helping the lame dog.

§ 2

Meanwhile what had been happening to disperse his old friends in Canonbury?

There was no fear that Tom and Mary would change, or that their children would grow out of their readiness for fun of any kind. They never 'grew up' in the usual sense of the word, but by the end of the seventies they were certainly getting bigger. From their appearance the four boys might have been the same age, only that the two younger ones were taller than the two elder. They made all sorts of friends, as young men do, and their school-fellows, past and present, as well as Tom's business friends were continually dropping in. They brought their sisters; and what with Cornish cousins staying for a few days and various acquaintances of Mary's, there was no lack of girl visitors. Mary welcomed them all, especially the girls. She had a settled policy in this matter: the greater variety of girls that the boys met in this informal intimate way the better chance there was of their not falling in love with some mysterious goddess. Their sister Molly was far too ignorant and young to be of any use in educating them along such lines.

Tom thought this policy a bit risky, but Mary contended that bringing up four boys was bound to be risky whatever you did; they were sure to make fools of themselves now

and again; better let them do it among the home acquaintances, and probably be laughed out of it; if they were kept
from going out as they liked and meeting whom they wanted
something more serious might happen.

Anyhow, this plan made life at Canonbury full of go
and interest. The boys at their various work in the day,
and always some amusements in the evening—singing,
cards, charades, dancing, with Charles making the piano
do anything he liked. The best dancer of all was Tom.
The best voice (when he chose to sing) was Tom's. A game
of cards seemed to have no fun in it without him. The
evening didn't properly begin until he had come home from
the City. Mary saw that there was plenty on the table at
meal times, but for the most part she sat aside and looked
on—a bit too old for dancing, she protested. One evening
twelve-year-old Molly came up to her with a bit of French
to be translated for her school homework. Mary didn't
attend to what she was asking, for her eyes were fixed on
Tom dancing with one of the girl visitors. Molly went
silently away, vaguely uncomfortable at the peculiar look
in her mother's eyes.

The same kind of vague discomfort seized her one day
when she heard Tom say, 'Don't you go and get married,
my boys, whatever you do.'

The boys laughed a ready assent, but Molly was horrified
to think where they would all have been if he had followed
his own advice, and she exclaimed, 'But what about you
and mother?'

'Ah, that's another matter. If you boys think that any
girl at all will come anywhere near your mother you are

making a ghastly mistake. Why, there is no one in the world to touch her, for learning, or looks, or ability, or anything you like.'

That sounded splendid. But children, more inarticulate even than animals, have the same uncanny consciousness that gets underneath the words and actions of sophisticated people. The adulatory words didn't undo in Molly's mind the effect of the strange advice to the boys.

§ 3

The summer holidays of '79 found the family more scattered than when the children were young. The eldest boy, Tom, was on a walking tour with an old Salopian schoolfellow. Barnholt, the youngest boy, was at sea, some-where near the Horn. Dym wanted to be at home to work at his mathematics. So when a letter came from Tony to say that there was to be a bazaar on a grand scale at Tehidy (a big estate near Camborne), and would some of the young people come down to liven it up, the only young people available were Charles and Molly. They both leapt at the idea. Charles didn't care much about the bazaar, but was full of schemes for sketching expeditions in Cornwall. Molly was all agog at the idea of actually selling things. Tony had suggested in the letter that there was to be a bran-pie, and this device when explained to Molly seemed to her a magnificent way of selling goods. The only thing was to wait till Tom came home in the evening to get his permission for them to go.

'Go,' said he, 'of course they shall. And I'm pretty well off at the moment—they shall go by the Dutchman.'

Undemonstrative as they were Charles and Molly nearly fell on one another's necks in their excited joy. To travel by the Flying Dutchman, which disdained third-class people, which left Paddington at 11.45 instead of 9—it was better than any fairy-tale they had ever read. The next few days were spent in preparation. Tony had insisted on their bringing some sketches to put on the Reskadinnick stall, so Mary and Charles began to look some out and mount them. Molly sought out some small treasures to wrap up into mysterious packages for the bran-pie, and bought a few extra ones from the stationer's shop near by.

When the actual morning came they almost wished they were going by the old 9 o'clock train. They couldn't believe that a leisurely breakfast and a dignified start just before noon would bring them to Camborne on the same day.

'If I can get away from the City I'll slip over to Paddington to see you off,' were Tom's parting words to them as he left.

And sure enough there he was on the platform, beaming and carrying a parcel. As soon as the tickets were taken, luggage labelled and corner seats found, he disclosed what was in his parcel. There were several little treasures for the bran-pie, tiny toys and some 'latest things' in the pencil and note-book line. But the chief capture was a dozen cards, on each of which were fixed twelve studs.

'Now these,' he said, 'you can sell at odd times in the bazaar. If you sell each stud for twopence, you will make quite a lot. I saw these cards going for fourpence each in a little shop I was passing, so you can see what a big profit there will be.'

'Yes, but,' objected Molly, 'is it fair to sell a thing for more than you gave for it?'

Tom laughed, and then explained to her that a man had to be paid for his time and trouble. 'You see I had to go down to Farringdon Market to get them, then bring them here, and you have to take them all the way to Cornwall. These studs will be a novelty down there, but there's just a chance that the people in the bazaar may turn up their noses at them, and refuse to buy them, and then where would my four shillings be? Gone.'

Thus briefly, and while the Flying Dutchman was pawing the ground, did Molly learn from her father the main points of supply and demand.

That journey was a memorable one for both boy and girl, for they didn't have such another jolly one for many a long day. Tom had also brought a magazine for Charles and a copy of *Helen's Babies* for Molly to read on the way. Not that they needed anything to pass the time, for the mere rate of the train was exciting enough.

It was still daylight when they arrived at Camborne, and they were hardly more tired than when they had started. Reskadinnick was full of preparations for the big event of the summer. Various aunts had made special aprons for the girl sellers—all befrilled and embroidered, and endowed with pockets for putting the money in. There was a preliminary day for setting out the stall, as full of bustle and fun as decorating the church, with picnic meals. Molly was busy stuffing her bran-pie, and printing a card for it—*6d.* a dip. Charles arranged the sketches to the best advantage, stepping back and putting his head on one side to see the effect.

The whole family was driven to the scene of action in a big wagonette, and all Camborne seemed to have come to buy. The studs sold like hot cakes, so that in the evening Molly raised the price to threepence each, having picked up for herself another point in economics. A long and triumphant letter was sent home the next day giving a full account of her successes, and wondering in a postscript whether another shilling pocket-money could be spared her, since she had been rather extravagant at other people's stalls.

§ 4

It was a Wednesday in late November of that year, a raw, chilly day, and Molly ran as usual into her parents' bed-room to say good morning. To her surprise she saw her mother lying on the edge of the bed, fully dressed and with a little red shawl round her head. She asked where her father was and what was the matter.

'I'm a bit worried, darling. He didn't come home last night. I watched at the window for a long time, and then came up here to try to sleep, but it isn't much use.'

'He'll be all right; he's called away somewhere. The post will be in presently and there'll be a letter, or a telegram or something. Don't worry.'

Dym and Charles, the only boys at home, were quite cheery about it at breakfast, and indeed showed great surprise at their mother's excessive anxiety—it was so unlike her.

'Did he say anything,' asked Dym, 'when he went off yesterday morning, about a chance of being late, too late for the last train, or something?'

'Nothing, nothing at all; he said nothing,' she replied in a strangely agitated way.

As soon as breakfast was over she announced her intention of going into the City to make inquiries, and this seemed to the boys a capital idea—far better than sitting in the window and worrying—not that there was anything to worry about they considered.

Molly was not quite so happy about her mother. She couldn't get out of her head all the morning the dreadful look on her face when she was caught unexpectedly lying on the bed. She ran home from school with the words on her lips 'Any news, mother?'

'Yes, dear,' she replied cheerfully. 'I went straight to Uncle Alfred's office in Coleman Street, and he told me that there had been an urgent business call from Doncaster, and that I should hear soon. So we must just wait.'

'Good. Doncaster. Well, if he was called away latish yesterday, travelling by night, busy to-day, he'll get off a letter this afternoon, and you'll have it to-morrow.'

Thursday morning, however, brought no letter, and during breakfast the boys found heaps of reasons why he might have just missed the post, carefully evading the question of why no telegram. Molly found it very difficult to attend to her lessons at school, or be as boisterous as usual in the playground. To her question 'Any news, mother?' on her return home there was only a shake of the head, and words of cheer stuck in her throat. When the boys came home for the usual jolly tea-time, conversation languished, and they all avoided each other's eyes. Somehow there seemed to be a great deal of work to be done that evening.

Friday morning came. Post again a blank. Molly didn't run home from school but lingered as long as she could, and didn't even ask if there were any news. Dym didn't come home to tea; he had said in the morning as he went off that he should stay on at school to get some extra coaching in mathematics. Charles and Molly were only too thankful when tea-time was relieved by the presence of a Cornish cousin and her niece who were living in the neighbourhood. Tiresome and stupid in the extreme, they were a godsend at the moment, and they were begged to stay on.

'Well, we mustn't be late. Your husband will be coming in soon, and we don't want to be in the way.'

'As it happens he has been called away, and may not be back till late,' said Mary. 'Let's have a game of cards, shall we?'

Mary knew full well that such an occupation would provide talk of itself and avoid tiresome questions. So the five sat down to a game of 'nap', which required no concentration, but a good deal of desultory fuss over 'going' and scoring and paying over counters, which were issued at a penny the dozen. Charles and Molly tried to be funny, but made little headway. Mrs. Tyack and her niece must have suspected that something was wrong, for they were deplorably soft-toned and unsporting, showing no genuine fervour about making tricks. Molly furtively watched her mother, vaguely sensing that she was getting near the end of her tether, although she took her part in the game—almost eagerly. Molly wished the ceiling would fall—anything to break the oppression.

It was Molly's deal. She tried to raise a laugh by hugging

the pack in her usual absurd way. There was a knock at the front door. Could it be? No, it was not the one they were aching to hear—Tom's familiar one of four short taps followed by one detached and decisive knock, that seemed to say 'here I am, me—Tom'.

Molly, heart in mouth, went on doggedly dealing, listening to Susan the housemaid hurrying up from the kitchen to answer the door. It was a relief (for goodness knows what was expected) when the familiar face of her Uncle Alfred appeared at the door. But instead of his usual jolly smile there was a hurried and awkward expression on his face, and he was accompanied by a complete stranger.

'Can we speak to you alone, Mary?' was all he said.

'Light the gas in the breakfast-parlour, Susan,' said she, rising immediately and following them.

Swiftly and tactfully the guests, Mrs. Tyack and her niece, faded away, leaving Charles and Molly alone in the dining-room. There must be some definite reason for the fact that absurdly irrelevant trifles seize our attention in a time of mental stress; perhaps they rock us to and fro until we get enough balance to face the inevitable. Charles and Molly stood by the fire, silent. At one end of the mantelpiece stood a plaster-cast of Faust and Marguerite. Molly stared at this ornament as if she had never seen it before and noticed that a piece of Marguerite's foot had been broken off. She was observing this intently when the most penetrating and unearthly cry seemed to swirl round her.

'Whatever is that noise, Charles?' she said. 'It sounds like outside. There must be an accident in the street,' and she moved towards the window.

'It isn't in the street,' said Charles in a frightened voice, 'It's in the breakfast-parlour . . . it's mother.'

Then followed a succession of heart-rending low moans. Then silence. The next sound to be heard was Uncle Alfred's voice at the top of the kitchen stairs, calling urgently for water.

'Mother must have fainted,' said Charles. 'He's either ruined or dead.'

For one moment a glimmer of hope sprang up at the idea of mere ruin, but they both really knew better.

'Mother would never mind his being ruined,' said Molly, and Charles nodded assent.

'What was that other man doing here?' she asked. 'I heard Uncle Alfred call him the Inquest man. What's that?'

'I think an Inquest is something they have when there's an accident—when some one's killed. But perhaps it's only when they are injured badly; I don't quite know.'

Just then Mrs. Tyack and her niece came into the room. They had not gone home but had hidden in the hall, and now they told Molly to put her things on and come back with them for the night. She didn't want to go, but it was kindly meant and Charles persuaded her, and said she could come home again first thing in the morning. They showed their sympathy by saying nothing at all, and putting her in a little room to sleep by herself. She got up, as soon as she decently could, and they let her go home when she had swallowed some breakfast. Home? Was it still there? She hastened up Grange Road, desperately hoping that it was all a mistake, or that her father was only injured rather badly.

But as she drew near the house she saw that the blinds were all down. She had heard that people did this when some one was dead, and she then felt for the first time the awful finality of the word 'dead'.

Dym was waiting for her and opened the door as soon as she began to knock, but said not a thing more than that mother was very ill, and no one of them was to go near her. He and Charles avoided Molly, probably fearing that she would ask questions they didn't want to answer. So, desperately desolate, she went down into the kitchen, that unfailing bureau of information. The servants were very kind, and mercifully talkative. They were clearly glad to tell all they knew. They told her that the poor master had been killed in crossing the railway at Barnsbury station. They had read the account of it in the newspaper on Wednesday, but as no name was given they didn't know who it was till later. If it had not been for the details they gave her, and they spared none, she would never have known the place and manner of his death. She saw in *The Times* that his age was forty-two, and that was all she ever learned. For in those days it was the custom never to mention the name of one who had died to those who loved him. Except with such bated breath that one naturally avoided it.

There seemed to be a large gathering for the funeral. Alfred arranged some kind of feast at Canonbury, and many voices could be heard and much coming and going. Dym, Charles, and their brother Tom, who had come home on purpose, took part in everything, but Molly saw no one. She was told to stay upstairs in the study, because her best dress was a brown one, and that wouldn't do at a funeral.

So she crouched on the ottoman in the window and waited, going now and again to the top of the stairs to listen to the sounds below. Once she ventured into a front bedroom to look out on that side for a change. There she saw, drawn up by the gate, a black carriage with black horses. Each horse had an enormous erection of black feathers on its back, and the carriage had several more on it. One look at the horrible sight was enough, and she hurried back frightened to the study, and waited for what seemed an interminable time.

Meanwhile Mary was lying between life and death, regardless of all her surroundings. With her, day and night, was Tony. No one appeared to know when she had arrived, but she was seen about the house at odd times, to fetch something for Mary or to give some direction to the servants. Like the boys, she seemed to avoid Molly, and once even, to the child's utter bewilderment, had snapped out (in answer to some mild question about something), 'It's no concern of yours.'

Grown-ups seldom seem to realize that withholding facts from a child does not prevent thoughts and misery, all the worse for being vague. An adored father dead, a mother too ill to be seen, and the aunt who had always been lavishly kind actually snubbing her. Molly had many more griefs in life, but never one so completely companionless. It was long years before she realized that Tony herself was overwrought, and that snapping out at some one had always been her safety-valve.

ELEVEN

THE FIFTH MAN

With Tony's constant help, and urged by the needs of her children, Mary was able to pull herself together and keep the home at Canonbury going for five more years. Then her boys were scattered, and then again for five more years she and Molly lived together, wherever Molly's work happened to be. They were more like sisters than mother and daughter, discoursing of everything under the sun, but with never a mention of Tom. It was during their long summer tramps together or their winter evenings over the fire that Molly learnt, bit by bit, most of what has already been related about Tony.

Although Molly didn't notice it at the time, she was aware on looking back that Mary was not very chatty about her own experiences, but was rich in reminiscences of Tony and the beginnings of her love story in Norway.

'I should have thought that *you* would have attracted Otto, mother; because Tony must have been so young then.'

'In years, yes, but in her ways and thoughts she was far more serious. Absurd as it seems she has always been more like the elder sister, saving me from many of my follies.'

'But Tony isn't so serious; she's jolly enough always.'

'That's true, but she is far more literary and poetical than I am, and she seemed to become actually Norwegian in her intense love for the country and its people and language and legends.'

'It was you who made her go to Norway with grandpapa once, wasn't it? That was like an elder sister.'

'No. I fear it was more of a childish lark on my part. But how thankful I am now that I did it. That was the last time she ever saw Otto.'

'How much older are you than Tony, mother?'

'A good bit.' She became vague at once. Any approach, however indirect, to the question of her age brought on this vagueness. After a time Molly's curiosity was aroused, and she would try to catch her with a sudden question, 'About how old were you then?' but she was too quick and would reply 'Oh, about the same age as other people at that time of life.' The plain question 'In what year were you born?' led her to tell a story of her brother William. On some occasion he had to be a witness in Court. He was asked his name, and then (rather too brusquely) his age. This he refused to give, maintaining that it had no bearing on the case. The lawyer was annoyed and after some other questions popped out 'In what year were you born, Mr. Vivian?' 'Ah,' said William, 'now if I told you that, you would be able, with all this spread of education, to reckon my age.'

So the subject of Mary's age became a little joke between them, and Molly never suspected that there was any reason for the reticence beyond a mere whim or a family idiosyncrasy. Somewhere about fifty was Molly's guess at her age. Her hair was very dark, almost black, with no hint of grey, and with a lovely glint of auburn when the sun caught it. Her sight needed no glasses. She was lithe and wiry, able to walk ten miles at a stretch without fatigue, and became ever more absorbed in her hobby of water-colour sketching.

Mary had often protested against the petition in the Litany
to be delivered from sudden death. 'It's far better than a long
illness,' she would say, but perhaps she altered her opinion
as time went on. It was for herself, and not for those dear
to her, that she considered sudden death to be a boon. She
had her wish, for it was after a short, sharp illness that she
died—quickly—as she had done everything else, leaving a
water-colour of a part of Barnes Common half finished.
Never for long years had she consulted a doctor for any
ailment, and she had always scouted the idea. But when
unaccountable pains became too frequent, Molly insisted on
calling in a doctor. An operation was needed, but the trouble
had been neglected too long, nothing could be done, and
in a few days she was dead. But she made her doctors laugh
almost *in articulo mortis*. She might have said with Sterne,
'Quand je serai morte on mettra mon nom dans le liste de
ces heros qui sont morts en plaisantant.' Her boys were
summoned, but arrived too late to see her. Not even Tony
had been able to come in time, and her daughter was the
only one to hear her goodbye words, which were characteristic of her. Speaking a little hurriedly, as if she were
just starting to catch a train, after spending a pleasant week-
end visit, she said, 'I must go—I must go—Be sure you are
good to Tony.'

There was no message for her boys, no solemn injunc-
tion to her daughter, but just this simple handing on of an
affection that had been the deepest thing in her life. From
the day of her birth Tony had been Mary's delight, her
intimate friend, her prop and stay in all her troubles one
after the other. Molly knew something of all this, and for

her own part needed no telling to 'be good to Tony'. Tony had been a second mother to her, and a bit more than even that. Tony was associated with the most joyful times of her life—the happy summer holidays at Reskadinnick. Tony had inspired nearly everything that the child and growing girl had attempted to do, and in her own undemanding way she had evoked an intense love in return. It was a love quite unspoiled by a sense of gratitude or any obligation at all. Tony was quite unlike any one else in her magic power of making people love her without exerting the least effort to bring it about.

When Mary died Tony came immediately and would have taken Molly home with her to Reskadinnick, but she refused, saying that she should feel her loss less if she went on with her work in London.

'You are right there,' said Tony, 'there's no consoler like the job you've *got* to do by to-morrow.'

Thenceforth Tony and Molly made up to one another for the loss of Mary by the closest friendship. Molly spent her holidays with her in Cornwall, and they wrote to one another about once a week. She was one of the few people who could write a letter. Mary, despite all her wit and enjoyment of life, could never write a letter that was worth preserving. Tony's every letter was seized with eagerness, for it was bound to contain something of interest. She would often begin without any formal 'dear so-and-so', plunging at once into what was uppermost in her mind, and she could make the most trivial incidents seem Homeric. Thus, for instance:

'You can't imagine the difficulties that beset me when I think I will write to you; for instance yesterday I rose early,

went in the dairy, unreamed the milk so that the pigs might
have an early breakfast, measured the new milk from the
heifer, took up what I allow for the house, and what to sell,
looked after my chicken, superintended dripping-toast for
William and Frances in bed, made two sponges, then had
breakfast, a most delicious plate of porridge, followed by
bacon that I had cut and put to cook. Well then I
shouldered my cloak and proceeded to inspect pigs, cows,
and calf (a real beauty) and what provender there was for
them. By this time I had to begin work—bread, seed-cake,
two puddings (dinner and supper), five pasties and other
little trifles, had my dinner (pasty) and retired to my virtuous
couch for a short rest, but presently heard downstairs a
well-known voice, a cousin and his son, who had been fishing all the morning, or trying to, and came on here to have a
dish of tea. Shifted my attire as quickly as possible, came
down, cut bacon and poached eggs for them; also cut
delicious new bread and butter. By the time they had
finished and gone I was done.'

'Outside the window I can see fifty chicks "scratching
up the lil island". Last night a lovely new brood of sixteen
were all, except one, killed by a stoat.'

She had the rare gift of stopping when she had done;
she never wondered or hoped, and if she mentioned the
weather it seemed to rain or blow or shine in your face
as you read. However short her letters, they were sure to
be crisp with adventure, tragic or comic; the extremely odd,
not to say suspicious, behaviour of old Mrs. Pendray; a
visit from the vicar with a joke that 'I can tell you, dear, when
I see you, but should not like to write down, or to repeat to

every one.' Now and again there would be dark hints of some trouble in the house, 'further news that had better not be told, dear'.

Always there was vivid interest in her niece's doings, with stern demands to know what sketches she had been managing, and exhortations to keep up her music. Her every letter made one want to sit down at once to reply—a sure test of a good writer. Nothing that was related to her was too trivial to draw forth some caustic or amusing comment. What a lucky man must Otto have been to get love letters from her.

Better than letters were the longed-for holidays, when Molly used to post straight to Reskadinnick as to her home. It was one summer afternoon, when she was wandering about alone, from orchard to mill, from yard to mowey, going over the jolly memories of childhood, that she came across old John Floyd. He had been a farm-hand ever since she could remember. He was leaning upon a stick by the horse-pond. She said 'good afternoon' and was passing on, not expecting him to know her. But he heaved up on his stick, evidently hoping for a chat, and began by saying how right sorry he was to hear of the death of her mother. Pleased to hear her mentioned, Molly listened with pleasure to his talk of how 'wonderful kind' she had been to him and his children.

'I suppose, John, that you can remember her when she was a girl, before she was married, when she was Miss Vivian?'

'Aye, when she was Miss Vivian, and when she was Mrs. Budge, too.'

'When she was Mrs. Thomas, you mean, John,' said Molly, smiling to herself at his funny mistake.

But no, in spite of her correction and even her reference to her own name, he insisted that she was Mrs. Budge. In fact the old chap was worried, and began to be even fretful at being contradicted. Molly couldn't think of any Mrs. Budge with whom he could be confusing her, although there were people of that name in Camborne. So putting his mistake down to the wandering of old age, she nodded acquiescence, and enticed his memory in other directions. In these he was quite sound.

Amid the many changes of family life at Reskadinnick, Tony had always kept her own bedroom. As mistress of the house she might well have chosen one of the ampler and more dignified rooms in the new part. But she preferred a little one which was bang in the centre of the whole structure, with one door leading on to the staircase of the new part, and the other leading by devious routes to the kitchen regions—a really strategic position. The tiny dormer window gave her a view of the side garden and pond with its great elms, while beneath was the side door, where all friends (except carriage folk or strangers) presented themselves, and where the postman delivered letters.

While the 'front kitchen' was the centre for family conferences, Tony's room was the place for secret confidences. Here Molly had loved to come as a child, to be shown all the treasures, mostly from Norway, that were locked up in the glass-paned cabinet, and handled with mystery and reverence. It was here that Mary had come so often to have her long talks, her jokes and griefs, with her beloved sister in former days. And here Molly used to come every evening of her holidays for a good-night talk.

On the evening after her chat with old John she went up to Tony's room as usual, and mentioned the meeting with him.

'He seemed to remember mother all right,' said she.

'Yes, he well might. He was rather a favourite with her. Sometimes he had to work far afield for a whole day, and he would come round the day before and hint as much. "All right, John, call in for your pasty," she would say. And you never saw such a pasty as she used to prepare for him— some fifteen inches long, and stuffed with anything that was going. It was a joke with us all—a John Floyd pasty.'

'Just like mother! You remember our "old man at the corner", the crossing-sweeper at Canonbury, that we children made friends with?'

'Yes, rather. Many's the penny the old chap had off me.'

'Well, mother used to send out a plate of dinner to him when we had a specially festive time. She used to say she couldn't enjoy her food when some one close by was short.'

'Did John say anything about the pasties?'

'No. To tell the truth I slid him off talking about mother. Poor old chap, I don't think he is long for this world.'

'Whatever made you think so?' exclaimed Tony, astonished. 'Why he is barely eighty.'

'Anyhow he's getting senile.'

'Not a bit of it, dear. He walks with a stick, 'tis true, but he's as good for a day's hedging as any one of his numerous descendants. Whatever made you think he was failing?'

'It'll make you laugh. He insisted that he remembered
mother when she was Mrs. Budge!!'

They were by the window looking out at the soft summer-
night sky. At the moment that Molly said the word 'Budge'
she was aware that Tony gave a slight start, and when she
went on to say 'Fancy! Budge! What a ludicrous name to
choose from his rambling memory, wasn't it?' Tony didn't
look round nor produce the expected laugh, but muttered,
'Yes, dear, very odd.'

A sudden suspicion seized Molly. Tony was a poor liar.
Whereas Mary would put off the inquisitive with an easy
laugh, Tony would usually betray that she was hiding something. She was hiding something now—obviously.

'What are you thinking about? What are you keeping
from me?' asked Molly.

'Nothing, dear.'

'Oh, all right. Since John is not senile he will be able to
tell me what he meant. I'll ask him to-morrow.'

'No, no, don't do that . . . I would rather tell you myself . . .
that is, if it must be told.'

'Why all the secrecy? It looks as if mother was married
twice—a bit of a surprise that we never heard of it, but
there's nothing disgraceful in it. Why did she never refer
to it?'

'Because there was nothing happy about it from start
to finish, and Mary was determined that none of you children
should ever know of it. If it hadn't been for old John's
remark the story would have died with her.'

'You must tell it me now, or I shall be imagining all sorts
of dreadful things.'

'They could hardly be more dreadful than the truth. You probably know that Mary was a very lovely girl—not just pretty—and was talked of as the beauty of the county. She had a ready wit, too, and was full of high spirits and fun. It was this rather than her beauty I think that made her so popular with all the young men we knew. She had her likes and dislikes of course, but she treated them all pretty much the same, and certainly gave no single one of them any encouragement.'

'Just fastidious, I suppose? I can well imagine that.'

'Yes. She had so much attention that she was quite proof against having her head turned with it. And always, as soon as any one made the least advance, she would stop it at once, and keep him at arm's length. She had a perfect horror of a flirt.'

'That I know well. She brought me up to regard a flirt as the wickedest thing on earth.'

'Sometimes her repulses were a bit brusque. No man likes to be snubbed.'

'That reminds me. She told me once how a young man had tried to kiss her, and got badly scratched by a long pin in her hair.'

'She told you that, did she? I am surprised, for in a way that was the beginning of all the trouble. She laughed at his annoyance, and the young man never forgave her. . . . His name was Budge.'

'Well, then, if that was the man who married her, he must have forgiven——'

'Wait. Let me tell you. Talk of forgiveness, I can never forgive myself for the part I played in that folly. As I said,

he never got over her laughing at him, and he was mean
enough to put it about that she was a heartless flirt. The
men knew otherwise—knew that she would never needlessly
hurt a man's feelings. But several of the girls in the neighbourhood were jealous of her, and were glad of any excuse
to run her down. There's no defence against jealousy.'

'But what have you to blame yourself about in all this?'

'The gossip reached me. Some busy cousins thought it
"as well to let you know what people are saying about your
sister". My folly was that I thought it best to give her a
hint as to what was being said—to warn her to be specially
careful.'

'But surely there was no harm in your doing that? It
seems the natural thing to do. Did you find out who it was
who had started the talk?'

'No, not at the time. I only wish I had—for then things
might have been different. I just told her, in as off-hand a
manner as I could, that people were saying she was given
to flirting.'

'She laughed at that, of course?'

'No. She flared up. I had never seen her really angry
before. At first I thought she was acting—just pretending
to be in a temper for fun. But I soon saw that she was in
deadly earnest. "What! a flirt! me!" she cried, "and you
tell me to be careful!" "You see," I said, "you have refused
so many offers of marriage." "That's not my fault. What
do people expect me to do? To accept the first man who
asks me, with becoming gratitude? Or to take the seventh
for luck? Or just to put them in a bag and draw out one at
random, trusting to Providence?"'

'I see her point,' said Molly; 'I suppose she didn't care for any single one of them?'

'Not one had caused her the least excitement, nor had she in the faintest degree led any one of them to think so—I can answer for that. Well, she ended her tirade with an indignant demand to know how she was to behave more *carefully* than she had done so far. I was a bit nonplussed, and could say nothing. After a silence she said in a dead calm voice, "Very well, then, I will change my behaviour. I'll marry the very next man that asks me." She was so quiet and matter of fact in her manner that I was relieved, feeling sure that at last she was joking, and could see the absurdity of the complaints against her.'

'So far as I see, then, you might as well have never told her about them at all.'

'Of course. Don't you see—it was that folly of mine that I curse myself for—a thousand times.'

'But you meant well.'

'*Meant* well! What's the good of meaning, if you can't use your common sense? I might have known that there was no possible course of action for her except the one she had always pursued.'

'Well, go on, tell me how she did behave.'

'Shortly after our talk there was a dance up in Camborne, and as usual we had our good-night chat in this room, passing our opinions on this and that. At last Mary said she must go to bed, and standing with the door open, just over there (I can see her now) she said, "I've promised to marry young Budge." "But," I gasped, "that's absurd—you don't love him—you can't love that fellow." "Of course I don't," said she, "but I vowed I would marry the first man that asked me, and he asked me to-night. He took me by surprise, or I should have staved him off." "But whatever made him ask you?" I said in bewilderment, "I'm sure he doesn't care for you." Mary shrugged her shoulders, "I think he was drunk. Don't ask me any more," and with that she went up to her own room.'

'But you don't mean to tell me that she actually did marry him?' Molly asked, 'surely Grandpapa interfered?'

'Interfered! My dear, you cannot imagine the scenes we had—the arguments, the implorings—all to no purpose. You have to remember that Mary had been hopelessly spoilt by her father all her life—never denied anything—accustomed to have her own way as naturally as having her breakfast. When she had made up her mind to do anything no power on earth could stop her. So the best face was put upon it. The young fellow belonged to a good family, and was in a position to be married at once; so married at once they were.'

'How horrible!'

'Yes, I think that the giving away of Mary to that man was the most painful thing in her father's life—a life that had griefs enough, goodness knows.'

'Go on, tell me how it ended, for of course it ended or I shouldn't be here now.'

'They went to live up in Camborne, not two miles away. She didn't come down to see us, and for some reason I could not bring myself to go up to see them. We at home told one another that possibly the marriage might turn out all right after all, and agreed to leave them alone, to say nothing about it, and if possible not to think about it.'

217

As Tony paused here, Molly said, 'Was there anything specially worrying about it, beyond the fact that they were not really in love?'

'Yes. We knew that he drank heavily, for one thing. And there were rumours of worse trouble that reached father.'

'What sort of trouble?'

'Never mind. You wouldn't understand, and it doesn't matter now.'

'But tell me quite quickly two things—is he dead now? and did they have a child?'

'He is dead long ago, and there was no child—nor chance of one, I should say.'

'That's a relief. I've been speculating on the awful chance that I might have been a Budge! But go on.'

'Well, they hadn't been married more than a few weeks, and we had heard nothing of them, when one night I was awakened by the sound of gravel being thrown up at this window. I jumped up to see what it was, and pushed open the window. A nasty night and raining. I made out a figure in the darkness. It was my darling Mary. Cold with fright and dread of I knew not what, I put a shawl round me and ran down to the side door and let her in. The remains of the log fire in the parlour were still glowing, and I blew them into a blaze with the bellows, and put a kettle on, before saying a word. After she had sipped the hot drink I gave her, and had warmed her feet, her shivering grew less, and she began to tell me something of what she had been through, but all in broken sentences. I can't remember all she said, but I'll try to give it you in some sort of order.

'You'll hardly believe it, but it was actually on her wedding day that he reminded her of how she had laughed when his face was scratched. She laughed again, hoping that it had now become a joke. He soon undeceived her on that point. He told her that he had vowed he would humiliate her for it. Apparently he had been nursing his anger in this senseless way ever since. As the wretched days went by the horrible truth dawned on her that he had married her for no other purpose. At last she asked him point-blank why he had ever asked her to marry him: "For a bet," was his brutal answer. Some other fellows had said when he was complaining of her haughty manners, "Why don't you propose to her?" and then added, "You haven't got the courage! You know she'll snub you!" So he bet them he would. He then added further insults about his astonishment at her accepting him—insults that Mary said she could not bring herself to repeat.

' "Oh, Tony," she burst out, "I then saw the wickedness of a silly vow, and knew that I had been just as bad as he was—in my obstinacy. Consequently I bore his insults in silence, and tried to behave decently to him. But my lack of anger seemed to madden him more, and he has been drinking heavily. Now and again he looked so murderously at me that I have kept a stout stick within reach, just in case——"'

'I hope to goodness,' Molly broke in, 'that you didn't let her go back to him?'

'Wait. I'll tell you what happened. Mary went on to say that on that very night she had gone to bed actually hoping that he would be too drunk to do any mischief. But he wasn't. She was awakened from an uneasy sleep by a spot of candle-grease falling on her face. What was her horror at seeing him standing over her like a fiend incarnate, with bloodshot eyes, trying to set the bed-curtains alight, and muttering that he had had enough of her ways, larding all he said with the ugliest words he could lay his tongue to. Fortunately he was too drunk to control the candle. She managed to slip out of the bed, run downstairs, seize a cloak and a pair of boots from the hall and get outside the house. She heard him stumbling down the stairs after her, so she waited to put on the boots till she was out of sight of the front door. Then, without having any plan beyond the moment she made her way down here, and woke me.'

'Whatever did you do, Tony?'

'While she was telling me all this, and much more which I can't possibly tell you, I had induced her to lie on the sofa, took off her wet boots and put dry stockings on her feet, and even got her to sleep a little. When she awoke we had to think what was to be done. Of course I decided that she must on no account go back. But she insisted that she had brought all the trouble on herself, and was going to see it through. "In that case," I said, "I'm going back with you. I can be determined too." Poor child, she made no objection to this, she was only too thankful for my company. So as soon as it was daylight I got some breakfast for us both, and we started off. I left a short note to say where I had gone, and that they mustn't be anxious.'

'What a wretched walk back that must have been!'

'Mary was not pitying herself. All the way she was blaming her folly in having come away while there was a danger of the house being set on fire, or one of the servants being attacked. They met us at the door with looks of relief. They had called the coachman to help them quiet the master, they said, and he was now in bed and not raving so much. He lived for about a month longer, but never recovered either health or sanity. With the help of the coachman when he was violent, Mary and I took turns at nursing him, and his death was a blessed relief for every one.'

'What did his people say to it?'

'They were as grateful as could be, and were always on friendly terms with us. But naturally they wished to forget the affair as much as we did. In fact every one we knew was kindness itself in never referring to it.'

'And Mary came home to live, I suppose?'

'Yes, and for several weeks she was ill herself. She had kept going while the nursing had to be done, and then collapsed. Her wedding ring was gone; she had flung it away when he told her why he had married her. She took her name of Miss Vivian again, and lived for years here at home quietly and happily. It is astonishing what a power she always had of recuperating and renewing her high spirits, due mainly, I think, to her power of laughing at things that would otherwise hurt or embitter. I envied her that gift. But any idea of marriage was abhorrent to her, as you may well imagine.'

'Now I see why mother kept her age a secret. She feared I should say "Fancy your not being married till you were nearly forty." And now I understand too why she so often impressed on me to be deliberate. No wonder. She had a story too (invented perhaps) of a girl who married a man out of pique, just to annoy another man. It seemed to me merely silly, but she was quite serious about it.'

'She would probably have told you the whole story about her own folly if there had been any danger of your making a rash marriage.'

'Did my father ever know about it?'

'That I cannot tell. There were some things that Mary kept completely to herself. And why not?'

TWELVE

JOHN

OLD age never touched either Mary or Tony. While Mary kept her dark hair, her wiry activity and her puckish spirits to the grave itself, Tony grew grey, racked with rheumatism, and dependent on her stick to cross the kitchen. But death had to snatch her away when she wasn't looking, leaving her only a few days' rest in bed at the last. She would have been glad to die many, many years before, but there was always something that simply had to be done. Her zest for life never diminished. It was while she was hobbling across the room in her eighties that she stopped to look out at the sky and exclaimed, 'How I should love to go up in one of these aeroplanes!'

She clung to all her ancient methods of household work —butter-making, poultry-feeding, cooking, and management of servants. If indeed this last can have been called management. The girls came young, remained to be married or grow old, and looked upon Tony more as a mother than a mistress. An occasional lapse from virtue she treated in a spirit of tolerance; her excuse being that if God could wink at wickedness (as the Bible asserted), why shouldn't she? In all cases requiring delicate handling she was one of those rare women who know everything or nothing as the occasion requires.

The little labour-saving devices that Molly brought her now and again from London she distrusted, or considered that they made more work than they avoided. One of these, however, was an exception. She used to get browning for her gravies and soups by putting a piece of sugar in an iron spoon and thrusting it into the fire to melt, getting her face and hand almost unbearably hot. A bottle of liquid browning savoured of magic and certainly seemed meretricious; but having once tried it with no ill consequences to the family, she fastened on to it with glee.

Her later letters were a curious mixture of optimistic accounts of her live stock and little parenthetical outbursts of anguish. 'Am glad you liked the cream. She is a noble cow. In fact there are two which the man says are as good cows as any that walk these roads. You ought to have a pot of cream every week, but, my dear, 'tis my meat, drink, washing, and lodging. I have been and still am quite ill and breaking up I think. I still get up in the mornings and do my work in a feeble sort of way and then am obliged to go and lie down on my bed. I am rearing, or trying to, the handsomest calf I ever remember, red, not a white hair, and black tip to her tail. Also sixty-three lovely little chicks of different sizes and age, also two good pigs. Next week I hope to buy four more. Yes, the dear king's death was a shock, but, as you say, how lovely to die in harness.'

In truth she couldn't afford to be ill, for her sister-in-law, William's wife, was now quite useless in the house, and moreover lowered the temperature by uttering ceaseless low moans. At last she was completely bedridden, as a letter from Tony indicated: 'Poor old Frances is just the same, with a nurse to see her every day—clean sheet and nightdress, with orders to burn the others. Too expensive, my dear, couldn't be done; but the washing is bad enough and we get wet Mondays week after week. As for me, my dear, they never think there is anything the matter with me unless they see me carrying my head in a basket.'

No emergency would have led Tony to have the washing done on any day but a Monday, shine the sun never so brightly. An *idée fixe* if ever there was one. The lines that Molly quoted to her as 'old' she regarded as modern laxity:

> *Wash on a Monday, you've all the week to dry,*
> *Wash on a Tuesday, not so much awry,*
> *Wash on a Wednesday, you've let two days go by,*
> *Wash on a Thursday, wash with speed,*
> *Wash on a Friday, wash for need,*
> *Wash on a Saturday, sluts indeed!*

According to this, as her niece pointed out, no day was definitely evil except Saturday. But Reskadinnick never knew any day but Monday. On the stroke of twelve on a Sunday night strange sounds would come from the servants' bedroom. They were getting up to prepare The Wash, and to put out the colossal tubs that seemed to fill the kitchen. The aftermath of the actual washing—putting out to dry, taking in, folding, damping, ironing, and airing—pursued their regular course through the rest of the week.

Saturday evening, however, was sacred from labour of any kind. At sundown the Sabbath began, marked by clean table linen for supper. Whether this ritual was Jewish, or a wider Semitic custom introduced by the Phoenicians no one knew, but it seemed to the young people that if Sunday began at sundown on Saturday it ought to end at sundown on Sunday; but it never did; Sunday had more than its share.

This custom was on a par with the washing ritual. It had no connexion with any religious sentiment. As for Tony, what religion she had was a natural grace, quite removed from any beliefs or obligations. But the literary charm of the Bible fired her poetic enthusiasm. One day Molly read her a bit of the famous description of the Phoenician merchantmen in the twenty-seventh chapter of Ezekiel. She became quite excited.

'Why, they are the people who came here to Cornwall! Go on, go on reading. How glorious to sail about the world like that, trading in all those lovely things. I think old Ezekiel was just envious, and sorry enough to pronounce their doom. Coming to the Isles and trading in tin— that's us—us actually in the Bible!'

'There's actually a description of a *mine* in Job,' said Molly, 'perhaps a tin mine—just listen to this,' and she read the beginning part of chapter twenty-eight.

'Well, I never saw that that was a mine before, although I know the passage well enough. How father would have relished it!'

'There are some good bits in the New Testament too,' suggested Molly.

'No, dear. I don't care about the New Testament. 'Tis very small potatoes after the Old.'

In fact she was a glorious pagan, not troubling to pay even lip-service to conventional piety. Now and again she showed a darker and even despairing side of her mind, but for the most part she followed a lifelong habit of revelling in

the sunshine and trees and in young animals of all description, and (far above all) in the people she loved. In one of
her last letters to Molly she wrote: 'Oh if I could only see
you and yours, even if you came playing a hurdy-gurdy at
the side-door!'

When actually with her Molly could generally talk her
into sheer hilarity. One sunny afternoon for instance she
led her on with the gambit:

'You've had a wonderful life, Tony, far more than many
so-called happily married people. You've had the devoted
love of one man, and really countless children. As for me
and the boys, I know we all have loved you better than our
own mother, and that's saying a lot.'

'Don't say it. Never say that. Nobody on earth was
equal to Mary. You children never knew her as I did. She
never talked about herself.'

'That's true. What are you laughing at?'

They were up in her bedroom for their chat, for Molly
knew that fuller reminiscences were likely to emerge as
Tony was handling her treasures, mostly gifts from Otto.
As she was speaking of Mary her eyes fell on a little square
of gold lace.

'What does that remind you of, Tony?' pursued Molly,
egging her on.

'When we were girls it was the fashion to wear little lace
squares like this on our head. In fact we weren't "dressed"
without one, and they were all kinds of colours. This gold
one was a special treasure of Mary's that she had bought in
Paris—faded now of course, but lovely when new. One
day, when Mary was out—at the hunt, I think—there was

a sound of visitors at the front door. I rushed up here to make myself respectable—couldn't find my best net any-where—so I ran up to Mary's room and captured hers—this very one—hoping that the visitors would be gone by the time she returned. Thoroughly pleased at my appearance in this net, attention-compelling, my dear, I went down to the drawing-room and made myself agreeable to the visitors. I remember thinking of that saying of somebody's about the assurance of being well dressed imparting a peace of mind that religion is powerless to bestow.'

'I know what you are going to say—Mary came home.'

'Yes, but how? As she was going up to her room in her riding-habit she glanced through the open drawing-room door, saw what had happened and making a long arm she tweaked her net from my head.'

'How dreadful for you!'

'Not a bit. Every one laughed, and a party that had been stiff before at once became natural and jolly. Better thought I than being well dressed, or than religion, is a sense of humour. But a more awkward thing happened on another afternoon. It was pretty much the same situation. Mary was out somewhere, and I was doing my best to keep the visitors entertained till tea-time. They were heavy going, and I was longing for Mary's return—or tea—praying for night or Blucher, you know. It was getting dusk when she came back, and as soon as she saw who the visitors were she guessed my difficulty, and sought to show her sympathy by giving me a violent pinch as she sailed into the room. Quite a good idea, but unfortunately her pinch was bestowed on a perfect stranger sitting with her back to the door.'

'I hope they laughed at that?'

'The victim didn't, but Mary did. She used to maintain that it is fatal to apologize, and she burst into some theory on the value of pinching as a nerve tonic—the latest from London.'

'She might have been more circumspect before choosing her subject for the operation though, mightn't she?'

'Circumspect! She didn't know then what the word meant. Sometimes her impulsive ways had absurd results. I remember once we were all going somewhere by coach, and had to be up by seven on a winter's morning. Mary was usually awake early, so she undertook to call us all. So indeed she did. It had seemed a short night when we heard Mary's voice, "Hurry up all of you, the clock has just warned for seven." We all scrambled out and stood at our doors to listen for the old grandfather clock out there on the stairs to strike. It was very cold and William was showing signs of disbelief, but it was too dark to see the face. At last it began to strike: one, two, three, four, five, six, seven (there! cried Mary), eight (sensation), nine, ten, eleven, twelve. But by this time objurgations were pouring forth on Mary, who had quietly disappeared.'

Something else in her cupboard caught Tony's eye, and she said, 'Do you remember old Betsy Polglaze, who used to come and sit in the kitchen and pour out her woes?'

'Of course I do. It used to be a treat to me to hear her groaning "I've a pain 'ere, and a pain 'ere, and a pain 'ere." And you used to go on with your work, throwing out a bit of pity every now and again. I suppose the poor old thing is dead now?'

'Well, if she isn't, as your uncle William is fond of saying, they've done an ugly trick on her—they've buried her alive. She must have been nearly a hundred I should think. Just for something to say I used to ask her every time she came "How old are you now, Betsy?" And year after year her answer never varied "I'm in me four score." '

'She couldn't have been eighty all the time. Was it just a fancy age she thought respectable or pathetic?'

'That's what I thought till I mentioned it to some one who told me that it is the usual thing among old-time country folk, who don't go in for niceties in number, to reckon their age by scores. They are in their second score as soon as they are past twenty, and remain in it till they are forty.'

'What glory it would be to reach a fifth score, wouldn't it?'

'I expect the old things lose count long before that. But I was going to tell you about one day when I was busy in the kitchen as usual, making butter or something. In tottered old Betsy, more bent than ever, and sat down as she always did on the old chair by the staircase. "How old are you now, Betsy?" said I beginning the regular litany. "I'm in me four score." "And how are you?" I threw out after a pause. Then she began "I've a pain 'ere," and so on laboriously touching various parts of her body. As I knew it all by heart I paid little attention, but carried on with my work. She had reached her foot when she suddenly leapt up and performed a fantastic high-kick dance across the kitchen. My dear, what a shock I had—I nearly dropped the pan of milk I was lifting off the fire.'

'Whatever was it? a fit of some kind?'

'No. It was Mary. She had dressed up, and completely took me in.'

'What a lark! I expect she would have tried some such game on us children at home, only that the boys were too much on the alert, always looking out for some fresh take-in. But now I come to think of it she did once take me in completely. It was when I was about fifteen. It was a Saturday morning, when I didn't have to go to school. "I want to speak to you rather seriously, dear," said she, "in fact I want to ask your advice. Come into the dining-room." I felt quite important at this, for my advice had never been required before. To give an air of reality to the scene she grasped in her hand a letter in a blue envelope.'

At this Tony looked up sharply and said: 'Yes, go on, dear, what did she say?'

'Well, she was silent for a bit, and then began "I've a letter here that came this morning—What would you say, darling, if I were to marry again?"'

'Yes, and what did you say to that?'

'To tell you the truth, Tony, I had quite a shock for a few moments. I thought she was in earnest. She looked so anxiously at me. But of course I recovered myself, and forced a little laugh—a dubious one, for I wasn't dead sure that she was joking.'

'Yes, and how did she take that?'

'Well, rather oddly, now I come to think of it. A jolly burst of merriment at my discomfiture would have been natural, but she remained silent and looked a bit disappointed. I suppose she had hoped for more dramatic protests from me. However, after a bit she gave a little laugh herself. Quite relieved at this I said, "You did act that well, mother. You really took me in." "Yes, darling," said she, "didn't I do it well?" and she stuffed the letter into her pocket. Fancy going through all that just for a bit of fun! But the funny side of it doesn't seem to strike you.'

'No, dear, not at all funny,' said Tony slowly. 'I knew pretty well what your story was going to be as soon as you mentioned the blue envelope. I too remember that envelope. Mary wasn't acting at all. It was real.'

'Good heavens, Tony, you don't mean to say that there was *another* man in love with her, and wanting to marry her?'

'Wanting to marry her! He had wanted to marry her ever since he was a boy of twenty.'

'I never heard a word of him. Who was he?'

'One of the best men that ever breathed. How we all wished that Mary would marry him—but it was no use.'

In response to Molly's urgent 'do tell me about him' Tony related at length the story of John Symons and his hopeless love for Mary. When she came to the incident of the book of manuscript poetry she went to a drawer and brought it out.

'How did you come to have this, Tony?'

'You may well ask. Of course it was intended for Mary, as you can see,' and Tony pointed to Mary's own writing in it and then to the final heart-broken entry. Then she explained how John had entrusted the book to her, to be given to Mary when she thought fit, and how she had promised to let him know everything that happened to Mary.

'I'm sure you kept your promise as well as you could.'

'As well as I could—exactly. It was not always easy. I couldn't bring myself to tell him about the Budge affair, knowing how it would worry him, and when it was over I was glad I hadn't. You see he was away from England most of the time, and wouldn't hear of it from any one else.'

'Well, after that, did you show Mary this book?'

'No. For a long time she was not in the mood for the slightest reference to love or marriage, as you may imagine. I did once say that I had heard from John, and she was glad to know that he was well, but showed no excitement, nothing to induce me to pursue the matter.'

'And how about him? Did he get married?'

'No. I hoped he would, and hinted as much in one of my letters. He said that he met plenty of pleasant girls, but they were so tame, you could always tell what they would say next. After all, he said, you can't expect a person to love the moon when they have loved the sun.'

'He must have been hard hit, poor fellow. And from what you say I gather that that was Mary's *sole* objection to him?'

'Yes; she maintained that it would be easier to live with some one who hated you than with some one who loved you too much. Poor child, she tasted the other.'

'But what an awful pity it seems. I feel greatly drawn to this John Symons,' said Molly as she turned over the pages of his writings and drawings. 'He must have been a charming man. And it seems almost too ridiculous that mother's only objection to him was his excessive love for her. She must have spoken to him very kindly when she rejected him, or he could hardly have gone on being so faithful to her.'

'Kind—yes—she must have been—she never did anything by halves.'

'I would love to know this John Symons. Is he alive still?'

'No, he died several years before she did, but not before his wound was healed a bit by——'

'Oh, now I remember,' interrupted Molly. 'You know mother's mahogany box, where she kept her specially sacred treasures? One day I was looking over these—a lace cap of Grannie's, letters from Grandpapa, baby Charles's coral rattle, the Prince of Wales's wedding favours, and so on, and amongst them I saw a black-edged visiting card, and pasted on it a cutting from *The Times*, recording the death of a Captain John Symons. I wondered why she had kept this, for I had never heard her mention such a person. Now, of course I see.'

'And do you mean to say that she never once referred to that early love affair, even when you yourself were in love?'

'Never a word. Perhaps she feared that I might have wished he had been my father! Not of course that I——'

Tony protested against this impiety with so much vigour that Molly half suspected her of harbouring the same desire.

'Your father captured Mary's love and admiration suddenly and completely. He was a new type of man, absolutely different from any one she had met before—and he seemed to strike every one in that strangely *fresh* and exhilarating way. Their almost absurd married life, varying abruptly from wealth to poverty, was just what Mary liked. If

anything she preferred the times of low water because
they got more fun out of it and were drawn closer together.
I've heard her maintain that security is a kind of premature
death.'

'Did you tell John about their marriage?'

'Yes, and about the coming of each of you children. He
seemed genuinely pleased at the idea of her happiness, and
showed special interest in our dear Barnholt and his going
to sea.'

'And my father's death, did you tell him about that?'

Tony shivered at the recollection. It was the hardest
letter she had ever had to write, she said, and even so she
had by no means told him all. 'No one shall ever know
what Mary poured out to me when she was delirious during
those dreadful days. Once I thought she was dying. I
knew she wanted to, and I almost wished it for her——'

While Tony was pausing here, Molly put in quietly,
'There's one thing I always wanted to ask, and never knew
how or when to ask, or whom . . . perhaps *you* know, Tony.
It's really of no importance—only my idle curiosity—but
did you ever know what my father was doing crossing the
railway at that odd station of Barnsbury? Perhaps it never
struck any of the others as curious?'

'I don't know at all,' she replied decidedly, and then
resumed:

'Well, to return to John, I told him the bare facts, and
then a little later told him how Mary was struggling along
to keep the home together for the boys and to get you
educated, and so on. After a year had passed he wrote to
ask whether the address at Canonbury still held good.'

'Ah,' interrupted Molly, 'now I see that that letter in the blue envelope was from him.'

'Yes, and Mary sent it to me to read. She was touched by it more than she could say. And well she might be. It was not at all a love letter in the ordinary sense of the word. He said quite shortly that his feeling towards her had never changed, and asked if she could bring herself to marry him. He was now retired, lived alone, and had a comfortable pension. He would see that her daughter had a good education, and there should always be a home for her boys to come to.'

'How splendid of him!'

'So she thought. But you can see how difficult it was for her. She was miserably ashamed of herself at having almost entirely forgotten even his friendship. She hated the idea of giving him only the tail-end of her life. She was glowing with gratitude for his generosity, and something more than generosity—and something more than gratitude, if you ask me——'

'Well, why didn't she——'

'It was touch and go. She was miserably undecided—a bit of pride, I think, partly, and a fear of what *you* would think, kept her back. At last she was driven to what amounted to a toss up. She would just see how Molly took the idea, and be determined by that.'

'Good gracious! Why on earth? How can people let their lives depend on such a thing? What could a raw schoolgirl know or judge?'

' Well, she knew how you adored your father, and what a happy picture there was in your mind of his love for her. She didn't want you to think she was unfaithful to his memory. Young girls are romantic, you know, and are apt to regard a second marriage as something almost disgraceful.'

'Why, *then* would have been the time to tell me that I myself was the result of a second marriage. Didn't that occur to her?'

'I doubt it. Anyhow, she would never have brought herself to give you that wretched story, after she had successfully hidden it for so long.'

'I can understand that, because there was no question of her ever having even pretended to love that first husband. But, Tony, do you think it is possible to be really in love more than once? In my own case I'm sure it isn't, but is it ever possible, do you think?'

Here Tony looked away, and after a few moments answered decidedly, 'Yes, I could tell you of a definite case.'

'Well, then, I feel sure it was so with mother. You and I and the boys all know how she loved my father. But I begin to see now that the knowledge of John's lifelong devotion brought back to her those early love scenes and——'

'She would have been stony-hearted if it didn't,' exclaimed Tony, 'and that's the last thing you would say of her.'

'Little things come back to me now . . . her peculiar fondness for *Persuasion* . . . how she used to love me to sing to her "Oft in the stilly night". She used to say sometimes, apropos of nothing,

> *Nous retournons toujours*
> *A nos premiers amours.*

It sounded like a quotation, but I believe she made it up.

Oh, Tony, why can't people seize happiness when it comes? Why are they such fools as to refuse it when it is actually spread out before them?'

'Rave away, you can't be too angry about it to please me. And you can put *me* in the same list of absolute fools, and cruel fools too.'

'Well, why didn't you do something about John and mother?'

'I did. At last the right moment had come, I thought, and I sent her this manuscript book to look at, and a letter of the strongest persuasion I could manage.'

'That ought to have had some weight—done something against the silly feelings of a schoolgirl. Though really if I had only been told a few *facts*, not even I should have been so silly. Why all this hiding up things?'

'You see, if once you begin to tell things a lot of the past may come up that is best forgotten, and then people may imagine other things that aren't true.'

'Well, tell me what Mary said to the manuscript book.'

'She acted impulsively as she always did, however much she might preach deliberation. She went straight down to Southampton to see John.'

'Oh, that was good. Did she write to tell him she was coming?'

'No. She used to say that when you have to face a meeting of any delicacy or have to say anything awkward, it is best to be entirely unprepared, and to trust to the inspiration of the moment. Prepared remarks, she thought, always sound unreal, while if you are unprepared all your character gets going.'

'And so much depends on what the other person says or does—do go on.'

'She went straight to the address in Southampton, but when she reached the front door she was seized with nervousness. The house, she told me, looked so dreadfully calm and unconcerned. She very nearly turned away again. However, she was determined not to be daunted and made a dash at the knocker—making it sound horribly loud. Her very name sounded unnatural as she heard the servant announce it at the drawing-room door. John had been reading at the open window with the sunshine pouring in from the West. As she went in his book fell to the ground and he was standing, clutching the table and staring at her.'

Here Tony lapsed into one of her silences, looking out of the window at her beloved elms. It was some time before Molly could bring herself to demand more.

'I had a long letter from Mary, and would read it to you but there was an order to burn it at once.'

'But you can remember some of it?'

'I remember that she went straight up to him, put her arms round him and kissed him—gave him the embrace that ought to have been given ages long ago.'

Again Tony lapsed into silence, and this time Molly was glad of it, for she was overcome by conflicting regrets and rejoicings. 'I would like to hear some more if you can remember it,' she said at last.

'Good gracious!' cried Tony, suddenly looking down into the garden, 'if some one hasn't gone and left the yard-door open, and there are the turkeys all over the begonia bed. My dear, I must go.'

POSTSCRIPT.—*The Rand Gold-mines of South Africa were worked at first almost entirely by Cornishmen, and there has always been a strong liaison in technical spheres between the Camborne School of Mines and Rand engineers. At one time the Cornish mines were the only comparable example in the world of the particular type of deep-level mining practised on the Rand. While the present story was in manuscript a grandson of Mary (named Barnholt after Otto) chanced to see in an ironmonger's shop in Johannesburg the word 'Reskadinnick' in beaten copper as a name-plate. It had been ordered and left unclaimed many years before. Barnholt knew it must refer to the family home, and bought it as a reminder of some Cornishman who had been as much devoted as himself to the grand old place.*

OXFORD

MORE OXFORD PAPERBACKS

Details of a selection of other books follow. A complete list of Oxford Paperbacks, including The World's Classics, Twentieth-Century Classics, OPUS, Past Masters, Oxford Authors, Oxford Shakespeare, and Oxford Paperback Reference, is available in the UK from the General Publicity Department, Oxford University Press (JH), Walton Street, Oxford OX2 6DP.

In the USA, complete lists are available from the Paperbacks Marketing Manager, Oxford University Press, 200 Madison Avenue, New York, NY 10016.

Oxford Paperbacks are available from all good bookshops. In case of difficulty, customers in the UK can order direct from Oxford University Press Bookshop, 116 High Street, Oxford, Freepost, OX1 4BR, enclosing full payment. Please add 10 per cent of published price for postage and packing.

SOME PEOPLE

Harold Nicolson

Introduction by Nigel Nicolson

A distinguished diplomat, journalist, politician, and author, Harold Nicolson provided us in *Some People* with a candid portrait of the English social and intellectual élite in the first quarter of this century. It tells the reader just what it felt like to be at Oxford in 1906, an insubordinate subordinate of the Foreign Office in 1911, or a guest at a Bloomsbury party in 1922. Almost from the date of first publication (1927) it was described as a minor classic, because it invented a new method of autobiography and perfected an idiosyncratic and highly attractive style, at once allusive, self-mocking, and pictorial. The book is an entertainment and much more. It is a careful self-portrait of an unusual man and an acute, sometimes mordant, commentary on human behaviour.

A PATH FROM ROME

An Autobiography

Anthony Kenny

At the age of 32, Father Anthony Kenny of the Archdiocese of Liverpool humbly petitioned Pope Paul VI 'to be allowed to return to the lay state'. Twenty years later, he is among the best-known of British philosophers and Master of Balliol College, Oxford. In this, the first part of what promises to be a remarkable autobiography, he describes his childhood, his training for the priesthood, and his growing doubts about the credibility of Catholic doctrine that began his journey along the 'path from Rome' into a wholly new secular life as a philosophy don.

'I have not enjoyed a book more for a long time. How does Kenny pull off this astonishing trick?' *Guardian*

'The story is told elegantly, coolly, and with agreeable touches of clerical humour' Don Cupitt in the *Listener*

'extremely moving' *Catholic Herald*

BLUE REMEMBERED HILLS

A Recollection

Rosemary Sutcliff

Rosemary Sutcliff is one of our most widely acclaimed novelists for children (and she has many adult admirers too). In *Blue Remembered Hills* she gives a moving account of the influences and the people that helped in her personal development as a writer.

'It is a remarkable book, not only for the clarity of her memory and for her determination to be honest, however painful the revelation, but also for her considerable powers of description' Caroline Moorehead, *The Times*

MARY, AFTER THE QUEEN

Memories of a Working Girl

Angela Hewins

In *The Dillen*, George Hewins described what it was like to grow up in Stratford-upon-Avon at the zenith of the Victorian age. His daughter Mary continues the story of the Hewins family in *Mary, After the Queen*, a spirited and touching account of the life of a working girl between the wars. Angela Hewins describes Mary's world of the factory floor, her friendships, and her struggle to make a living, when she found herself, in the 1930s, unemployed, and with a baby on the way.

'a touching and charming book' *Sunday Times*

'the whole of Mary's account has a lyrical quality. This is Angela Hewins' achievement. She has re-created the rhythms, the poetry of working-class speech.' *New Society*

A LONDON GIRL OF THE 1880s

M. V. Hughes

When *A London Child of the 1870s,* the first book in Molly Hughes's trilogy about growing up in Victorian London, was published in Oxford Paperbacks, Benny Green in the *Spectator* described it as 'literally unforgettable', and went on to say: 'It is always an event worth celebrating when an outstanding book, long neglected, is given a new lease of life by a sympathetic publisher, so I doff my cap to Molly Hughes on her return to print. She should never have been out of it.' The second book of the trilogy, the charming and delightful *A London Girl of the 1880s,* first published in 1943, is now also made available in paper covers.

STILL GLIDES THE STREAM

Flora Thompson

Like her well-loved trilogy *Lark Rise to Candleford,* this book depicts the vanished life of the countryside which Flora Thompson knew as a child in the 1880s. Cast in a fictional form, it is an enchanting portrait of an Oxfordshire village and its inhabitants around the time of Queen Victoria's Golden Jubliee.

'reading it is a perfect pleasure' Benny Green

LEAVES OF THE TULIP TREE:

Autobiography

Juliette Huxley

It was as a governess at Garsington, Lady Ottoline Morrell's mansion outside Oxford, that Juliette Huxley met the glittering Bloomsbury set, and among them her future husband Julian Huxley. She recalls the excitement and occasional chaotic moments of their courtship, and their later life together in London. She also describes with affectionate humour friendships with D. H. Lawrence and Frieda von Richthofen, Aldous and Maria Huxley, and H. G. Wells.

'This is the story of a real-life Jane Eyre, her romantic courtship and stormy marriage to a brilliant masterful and ruthless Mr Rochester.' *Observer*

'Against a background of two World wars and enormous social change, Juliette Huxley's autobiography has a fascinating and at times sad immediacy.' *Times Educational Supplement*

Oxford Letters & Memoirs

A LONDON CHILD OF THE 1870s

M. V. Hughes

Molly Hughes's account of growing up in London in the 1870s ranks with Flora Thompson's best-selling *Lark Rise to Candleford* and *Still Glides the Stream* as a classic description of life in Victorian England. But whereas Flora Thompson describes the rural, Molly Hughes describes the urban scene. *A London Child* was first published in 1934, and the reaction of *Country Life* remains valid today: 'The book has the charm of simplicity and frankness with faithfulness to fact and impression, and is delightfully human.

A YORKSHIRE BOYHOOD

Roy Hattersley

Roy Hattersley's engaging account of his boyhood has already been acclaimed as a classic of its kind. Born in Sheffield in 1933, he was a somewhat precocious only child. His memoir takes us through the hardships of the Thirties and the Blitz, and into the 1940s when he passed the eleven-plus examination and entered Grammar School. All the pleasures and pangs of a northern working-class childhood are evoked with wit, elegance, and candour.

'moving, funny, charming and enormously readable' *Listener*

'impressively candid and agreeably revealing' *New Statesman*

'A narrator who has the common touch . . . this gift for re-creating his childhood makes Mr Hattersley the Beryl Bainbridge of English politics.' Blake Morrison, *Observer*

A LONDON HOME IN THE 1890s

M. V. Hughes

This is the third book in Molly Hughes's delightful autobiographical trilogy. Readers of *A London Child of the 1870s* and *A London Girl of the 1880s* will eagerly take up the story where *A London Girl* left off. But this book can be equally enjoyed in its own right by the reader discovering Molly Hughes for the first time. Now a confident, literary-minded young woman, she becomes one of the first lecturers in a teacher training department at Bedford College, travels extensively, and is married in the year of Queen Victoria's Diamond Jubilee. She describes both light-hearted and serious domestic details, including her shopping expeditions in the Portobello Road, the birth and tragic death of her daughter, and the election campaign in which her husband stands against Lloyd George for the constituency of Barnet.

FIRST CHILDHOOD AND FAR FROM THE MADDING WAR

Lord Berners

'Aesthete, artist, and wit, Lord Berners grew up among fox-hunting philistines and attended a prep-school where excellence at games, to which he did not aspire, provided the only refuge from a sadistic headmaster. *First Childhood* is a wry record of his early kicks against the pricks, while *Far From the Madding War* is a delightful novella set in wartime Oxford with a thinly disguised self-portrait which anticipates Nancy Mitford's Lord Merlin.' *Books and Bookmen*

'Lord Berners spices his very funny account of a rather isolated and unhappy childhood, *First Childhood,* with a wicked wit.' *British Books News*

'It is a bargain and a delight—particularly the autobiography . . . by any standards an absorbing book.' *Times Literary Supplement*

A LONDON FAMILY BETWEEN THE WARS

M. V. Hughes

The Hughes family—a widow with three sons—were not well off financially, but were rich in affection. This is a gentle, often humorous account of a family growing up in the rural environs of London in the 1920s and 1930s. It recaptures the charms of a now vanished world, in which *The Times* arrives by bicycle, household necessities are supplied by a hawker with a pony cart, and making a telephone call is an adventure.

A KIND OF MAGIC

Mollie Harris

'has a special charm. Ms Mollie grew up in the Oxfordshire village of Ducklington in the 1920s, and reading about it gives a picture of rural life that, though only sixty years ago, seems like a pre-Fall idyll compared to present technological day.' *Books and Bookmen*

'Charming reminiscences of reassuringly eventless days in an Oxfordshire village by Martha Woodford of "The Archers". Hopscotch, daisy chains, lotions, potions, and primitive two-hole privies.' *Sunday Times*

'There can be few who possess such a gift of recall and talent for expressing experiences in words that Mollie Harris fortunately does . . . a nostalgic book for everyone.' *Cotswold Life*

'The pose is honest. It exhales authenticity, so by the time you reach the last sentence you feel you have occupied a warm corner of someone else's past . . . fine, original and lingering look back over gone-forever countryside.' *Herald Express*

ANOTHER KIND OF MAGIC

Mollie Harris

In this sequel to *A Kind of Magic* Mollie Harris describes her journeys on foot and by bicycle over the hills and through the villages of the Cotswolds, and recounts the hilarious country tales she was told by the people she met. In these anecdotes the local characters spring vividly to life: Mark the shepherd with his thousand sheep, Charlie 'Douser' the fireman, Old Jack the gardener, and many others. She also includes recipes in her book for such local delights as gingerbread, raspberry preserve, and elderflower champagne. This collection of anecdotes and country lore will entertain and captivate all those who cherish the countryside of England.

DECEIVED WITH KINDNESS

A Bloomsbury Childhood

Angelica Garnett

Angelica Garnett may truly be called a child of Bloomsbury. Her aunt was Virginia Woolf, her mother Vanessa Bell, and her father Duncan Grant, though for many years Angelica believed herself, naturally enough, to be the daughter of Vanessa's husband Clive. Her childhood homes, Charleston in Sussex and Gordon Square in London, were both centres of Bloomsbury activity, and she grew up surrounded by the most talked-about writers and artists of the day—Leonard and Virginia Woolf, Roger Fry, the Stracheys, Maynard Keynes, David Garnett (whom she later married), and many others.

'Anyone who vowed never to read another word about Bloomsbury should relent over this book.' *Sunday Times*

'written with enormous verve and startling honesty' *London Standard*

'A fascinating and very painful story.' *Tablet*

A COUNTRY CALENDAR AND OTHER WRITINGS

Flora Thompson

Selected and edited by Margaret Lane

Illustrated by Clare Roberts

Admirers of Flora Thompson will welcome this volume of her writings selected and edited from her uncollected or unpublished papers. It includes Margaret Lane's biographical essay; *Heatherley,* a lightly disguised account of Flora Thompson's life in Grayshott, Hampshire before she married; a selection of her observations and other writings; some of her poems; and photographs and line drawings.

'A must for Flora Thompson addicts and a superb introduction to the uninitiated.' *The Times*

THE DILLEN

Angela Hewins

George Hewins was born in a Stratford doss-house at the zenith of the Victorian age. Barely literate and undersized (hence his nickname, 'the dillen' or runt) he possessed an extraordinary gift: he was a story-teller of genius in the old oral tradition. The tale he tells is *his* tale, and the tale of those he met from the 1870s to the aftermath of the Great War, recorded by his grandson's wife as he approached his hundredth year.

'a Warwickshire Decameron' *New Society*

'It is funny and heartbreaking by turn, packed with incidents and curiosities.' *Sunday Times*

'It takes the reader by the scruff of the neck and forces him to taste the food, smell the smells, agree to the tricks and breathe the air of a cheerful, dreadful England which would do for you if it could' *Ronald Blythe*